The Robots Are Here!

The Robots Are Here!

by

D. S. Halacy, Jr.

W · W · NORTON & COMPANY · INC · NEW YORK

LIBRARY OF CONGRESS CATALOG CARD NO. 65–18047

All Rights Reserved

Published simultaneously in
Canada by George J. McLeod Limited, Toronto

Printed in the United States of America

3 4 5 6 7 8 9 0

Contents

ENIAC, the world's first "electronic brain."

"TransfeRobot," the assembly-line robot that pays union dues.

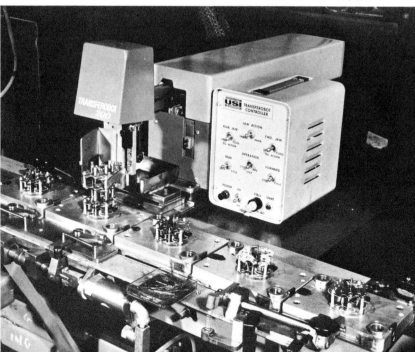

1

The Robots Are Here!

In 1946 two men named J. Presper Eckert and John Mauchly built the first electronic computer. By 1962 this "giant brain" had made such an impact on our society that Eckert said he hoped we would soon solve the problem of racial integration, for another kind of integration was going to be just as difficult to solve—the integration of man and machine.

About the time Eckert expressed concern over the problem of machines, an unusual event gave emphasis to his remarks. Among new payers of union dues in 1962 were a number of assembly-line robots. Each of these began to pay from twenty-five to a thousand dollars a year as it started its job in one of various factories in the United States. The money went into a fund for studying the problem of human workers versus automation. It is no longer correct to say that the robots are coming: they are already here in great numbers.

Robots did not burst into our midst in 1962. We have been using some mechanical workers for some time, including robot traffic policemen, and robot pilots in ships and aircraft. Newer machines are now being put to work in banks and businesses to handle facts and figures faster and better than humans can. The robot today is an important factor in our lives; tomorrow it will become even more so.

The automatic machine has not always been called a robot.

THE ROBOTS ARE HERE

Before being christened with that name it was known as everything from helpful friend to heartless enemy. The steam engines of James Watt, for example, were called "Iron Angels" by some and "Black Devils" by others. Less emotional names include *homunculus*, android, automaton, mechanical man, and *homo robotensis*. More important than the name, itself, however, is an understanding of its meaning.

The dictionary defines a robot as a brutal, efficient, insensitive person; an automaton. The word itself came into our language from the Czechoslovakian by way of a play written in 1921, *R.U.R.*, by Karel Capek. *Robota* is the Czech word for compulsory servitude, and the author called his artificial men robots.

In the play the robots were given human characteristics, and they ended by killing their human masters. Such a theme was not new in literature, but the play was important because it gave the mechanical man a name that has stuck. The dictionary lists such associated words as *robotism*, *robotistic*, *robotize*, and *robotry*.

Unfortunately the robot is often thought of as a mechanical monster, guided by an evil brain and bent on the destruction of man. In many movies and stories robots run amuck with all sorts of terrible consequences; we seem to enjoy sitting on the edges of our chairs and being scared to death by tales of malevolent mechanical monsters. The robot's literary reputation is an old one, as we find on looking back through writings even of ancient times.

In addition to knowing what a robot is and something of its history, we should also have an idea of the mechanisms

Bell Telephone Laboratories

Engineers double check a computer built from information furnished by another computer!

that make it work. Robots, like living creatures, need certain basic parts to function the way they are supposed to. Like us they need energy, muscles, and "brains."

There are all kinds of robots. The simplest are like wind-up toys, but others can even be made to respond correctly to a changing environment. (Such "adaptive" robots use a principle that is of vital importance to living things too.) We will learn more about the robot's "inside story" in a later chapter. Many robots built in the past were hardly more than toys— but toys of a wonderful and very special nature. Today some robots are built merely as stunts or for display or entertainment, but most exist to do a useful job. Their tasks are many and varied: from washing dishes to operating a remote weather station; from piloting an airplane or guided missile to handling dangerous radioactive materials that would kill human workers. The discovery of atomic energy has opened up challenging new fields for the robot, as has the exploration of space.

As part of the industrial revolution the robot has helped bring about automation—which is sometimes called the "invisible robot." Mass-produced themselves, robots staff factories that automatically turn out other products we need. These individual automatic machines, together with the electronic controls that operate whole factories, constitute the robot of automation. Robots come in all sizes: as small as the air-conditioning thermostat in our homes and as large as entire steel mills.

One type of robot we will discuss depends on the brain of its human operator, and some robots don't have any "brains" at all. But industrial robots quickly "learn" a variety of tasks and never "forget" them until told to do so. Some robots consist almost entirely of electronic "brains" capable of great speed and reasoning ability. Once so huge they were rightly called "giant" brains, thinking machines have shrunk in size until optimistic robot builders now foresee them approaching the human brain in compactness.

A lively argument goes on among scientists and engineers as to whether or not a robot chess player will one day be champion of the world. But a more basic question is why machines should be playing games at all!

Most robots *are* busy at workaday chores but some seemingly while away their time playing games such as chess, checkers, ticktacktoe, and even matching pennies. Games are really problems, and the robot that can play games can also solve other problems. Matching pennies, for example, is a practical application of the laws of probability and the simple idea of "heads or tails" leads to the mathematical field of "game theory." This theory has important applications in business, science, and war strategy.

Most robots have their brains "wired" in just the way needed to do their tasks, but some newer ones can "learn" from experience. And scientists studying this ability are learning something about the operation of human brains at the same time.

The robot is no longer a fantasy inhabiting only our dreams, the movies, and science-fiction stories: the *real* robot proves far more interesting than its imaginary counterpart. Robots serve us every day, often doing things we could never hope to do. But it is shortsighted to be blinded by the benefits of the robot and not to see the serious problems it creates at the same time.

Historically men have feared the robot as a stealer of jobs, and today the specter of "technological unemployment" is clouding the bright new world of machines. Many people in this and other countries have been displaced not by war, but by robots that have eased them out of their jobs.

Some men fear the robot as far more menacing than just a job-stealer. They think that machines will actually take over and run things; that man will become a victim of his own clever mechanical creations and vanish as the dinosaur did!

Opposing this fear is the idea of a peaceful joining of man and machine, with the machine freeing man from chores like digging ditches and "making marks on paper," so that he can devote himself to solving the truly important social and cultural problems of our time.

This is the problem of integration that Dr. Eckert, inventor of the electronic computer, was talking about. We can hope that the robot itself will help solve the problems it creates, for we need it desperately in our heavily populated and technologically complex world. Civilization with its banking, business, communications, manufacturing, and food-producing requirements is about to burst its seams. Already the robots are helping in these areas. Intelligently used, they can do much more. Perhaps some day in the future robots can even make war unnecessary, or at the very least club each other over the heads while humans sit at home in safety!

2 ·

Family Tree

We are inclined to think of the robot as a product of our mechanized and electronic age, but this is not the case at all. The robot has been with us not just hundreds, but thousands of years. The idea of an artificial creature endowed with the attributes of life seems to be almost as old as man's fertile imagination, and as far back as our literature goes we find mention of robots.

Homer's *Iliad* describes golden, three-wheeled mechanisms that served as information carriers for Hephaestus—the Romans called him Vulcan—Greek god of natural fire and metalworking. These robot messengers had wheels of pure gold and "handles of curious cunning." Hephaestus also presented a mechanical man named Talos to King Minos of Crete. This brass robot patrolled the island of Crete, hurling huge stones at fleets foolhardy enough to try an invasion. The fate of Talos is interesting; he was "killed" by Jason's wife Medea, who pulled a plug from the robot's foot and drained his power from him.

Daedalus, that versatile genius who flew with artificial wings, is also said to have built robots. Plato tells us these mechanical men were so successful they had to be tied down to keep them from running away. Among Daedalus' robots was a wooden Venus that not only had arms but could move them in a lifelike fashion because they were filled with mercury. Heron, writing in the second century before Christ, described a hundred or so robots, including a group of "singing gods and maids." Two hundred years earlier than this, the Greek Archytas built and flew a wooden "pigeon." Hebrew lore includes manlike beings called *golems* that sometimes ran amuck with terrifying results. According to legend, a man who knew the secret name of God whispered it to a *golem* made of clay, and the figure came to life. But this servant proved more dangerous than helpful and beat its master unconscious before it could be made inanimate again. And in "The Sorcerer's Apprentice" a magic broom overdoes a good thing when lazy apprentice Fritzl can't remember the words to control it.

There are astounding bits of prophecy too, in literature. Ali Baba's well-known "Open Sesame!" might have inspired designers of automatic electric-eye devices. Not so familiar is the Icelandic saga, *Frithiof*, written in the fourteenth century, long before the robot pilot. Frithiof needed no helmsman on his wonderful ship; the lucky sailor simply told it where he wanted to go.

EARLY AUTOMATONS

Somewhere between myth and reality are the "androids" of the monk Albertus Magnus of the thirteenth century. The name comes from the Greek words *andros* and *eidos* meaning "man-form." Magnus worked for thirty years to perfect his mechanical man. This robot was said to have guarded Magnus' door at the monastery in Cologne, greeting visitors and asking their business. Unfortunately the great churchman Thomas Aquinas, a student of Magnus, was so aghast at a mechanical man that he smashed the android to bits in righteous anger. We wonder how St. Thomas would feel if he knew that electronic brains are today studying his writings!

Robert Bacon also built a robot "Iron Man" in the thirteenth century. Two hundred years later Johann Muller went to the other extreme and built an "Iron Fly," and later a mechanical eagle that flew for Emperor Maximilian I at Nuremburg.

Artisans of old contrived some amazing androids, automates, or living dolls, as they were variously called. In colonial America dealers exhibited elegant clocks which not only told the correct hour but also presented the viewer with tableaux, like that of Herod lopping off the head of John the Baptist while his stepdaughter stood by with a silver platter. A happier looking automaton was a miniature juggler dexterously tossing three colored balls.

Still on exhibition today are the eighteenth-century androids of Pierre Jacquet-Droz and his son Henri-Louis. In the Fine Arts Museum of Neuchatel, Switzerland, three of these clock-work figures demonstrate their talents each month. "The Writer," a three-foot youth, dips his pen in an inkwell with a flourish and proceeds to write upon a sheet of paper. His body movements are realistic, his eyes follow the careful strokes of the pen. He can be adjusted to write whatever words are chosen; a typical message is "Welcome to Neuchatel." When the letters have been nicely formed, the robot penman dusts his finished product neatly and relaxes.

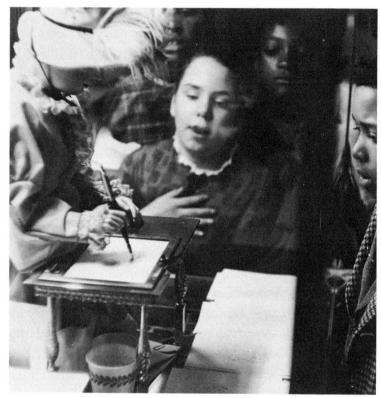

The Maillardet writing automaton on exhibit at Philadelphia's Franklin Institute.

Another android, "The Artist," draws the figures of Louis XVI and Marie Antoinette with appropriately artistic gestures; and a third, "The Lady Musician," plays charmingly on a spinet, her actions lifelike even to her breathing.

Philadelphia's Franklin Institute exhibits another lady android, made by Henri Maillardet, who worked with Jacquet-Droz. This one draws and writes. In the nineteenth century,

Drawing of ship done by the automaton.   *The Franklin Institute*

automaton-maker J. N. Maskelyne of London built similar figures including those of "Zoe," who drew pictures, and "Psycho," who played cards and did simple mathematics.

A mechanical duck was among the most perfect automatons ever produced. The work of Jacques de Vaucanson, this rare French bird quacked, bathed, drank, and ate in a

Sample of the automaton's penmanship.   *The Franklin Institute*

manner some called more lifelike than the real thing. So completely was the duck patterned after life that its digestive tract and bowels worked. The duck performed all over Europe and one of its biggest successes was on the stage of La Scala opera house in Milan.

There seemed no end to the tricks these nineteenth-century mechanical toys could do. Among them was a tightrope walker made by the Frenchman Robert Houdin. But for sheer complexity nothing matched the "Microcosm, or the Universe in Little" of Henry Bridges in England. This tiny replica took twenty-two years to build. Exhibited in Europe and the United States, the Microcosm consisted of the celestial bodies, a concert of the nine muses, Orpheus in the forest, a woodworking studio, a grove of trees, and a beautiful countryside with a view of the sea. The mechanism of gears, levers, and shafts that operated this tiny "universe" contained thousands of handmade parts.

The idea of a talking robot goes far back in history and even farther in legend. Heron described singing automata more than two-thousand years ago, and we have also mentioned Magnus' speaking robot. About A.D. 1000 Pope Sylvester II constructed a "talking head" with the power of mechanical speech. The German Friedrich von Knauss, who built a writing automaton in 1753, in 1771 turned his attention to talking heads which were considered marvels. We can understand why audiences looked on these early manlike robots not with amused wonder but with an uneasy feeling that perhaps these creations had been endowed with life itself. In that period, however, mechanical men were built *only* to impress and entertain. They had not yet begun to threaten men's jobs.

Despite the marvelous performances of the early automatons they were the simplest kinds of robots. In fact, the admirable consistency of their clockwork gears and levers may well have been their charm. A character in *The Road to Oz*, a mechanical man known as Tik-Tok, was admired because he always did what he was wound up to do. However, the idea of an automaton capable of more than routine actions gradually began to attract attention.

The British robot Psycho played cards, but when the Von Kempelen Chess Automaton began touring Europe late in the nineteenth century, the world was agog. Sporting a Turkish turban, and with great skill, the robot chess player bested some of Europe's crowned heads before it was caught cheating. Inside the boxlike machine was found a perspiring midget who had pulled appropriate levers to move the pieces on the board! But by 1914 a Spanish inventor named Torres y Quevedo had built a real robot chess player which was capable of a game limited to only a few pieces.

STORYBOOK ROBOTS

Edgar Allan Poe was among those who exposed the Von Kempelen fraud. Author Ambrose Bierce later fictionalized the idea of the chess-playing robot in his story *Moxon's Master*—about a similar machine that strangled its human opponent rash enough to defeat it in a game.

Bierce was not the first author to look with alarm at the mechanical man. In 1818 a twenty-one-year-old author wrote a novel with the same theme: the wife of the poet Percy Bysshe Shelley, Mary Shelley, is remembered in her own right for *Frankenstein*. In this book, Dr. Frankenstein creates a monster in the form of a man, and in so doing makes a big mistake. Endowed with man's most trouble-making characteristics—emotions—the frustrated robot turns on his maker and others. Such monsters weren't yet called robots; Mary Shelley called Frankenstein's creation a "daemon." The name robot had to wait for that grim satire on machines, the play entitled *R.U.R.*

International Business Machines Corp.
Early key punch machine, forerunner of modern business robots.

In Capek's play a factory produces artificial men. Real men would have to work no more; robots would do their chores.

The robots were tireless, efficient, and unfeeling. They were cheap and they worked for nothing; surely, the fictional robot builders thought, in ten years human labor would be obsolete. But such was not the case. In an effort to improve on their artificial serfs the designers added dangerous human qualities not present before. As a reader of *Frankenstein* could have predicted, the robots turned on their human masters and exterminated them. Not human labor, but humans *themselves* became obsolete in the play.

French writers too have been loud in their warning against such machines. Among French stories deploring the advance of the robots were Romaine Rolland's *Revolt of the Machines* and George Bernanos' *France Against the Robots.*

The movies featured robots early, and one pioneer film was Fritz Lang's *Metropolis*, with a mechanical *woman* in a starring role. Another robot film, *Der Golem*, was produced in 1915. A modern robot, built by Westinghouse and named "Elektro," acted in *The Day the Earth Stood Still.* Another mechanical man called "Robby" was the star of *Forbidden Planet.* A recent film titled *First Spaceship on Venus* featured an appealing little robot whose accomplishments included playing chess, and even being scared!

THE ROBOT GOES TO WORK

While robots were only interesting toys they were not really frightening. But the fears of fiction writers slowly began to come true as machines began to do useful chores, and do them better, faster, and more cheaply than humans could. It is often hard to tell which came first—a writer's concept, or an actual model he may have used for his story. Eli Whitney and his cotton gin were contemporary with the infamous Frankenstein monster. While Whitney was not menaced personally by his creation, he did have trouble with the human workers it threatened to displace.

The rock throwers who plagued the cotton gin (and a century or so later would attack the Rust brothers' cotton picker) had precedent for their angry action. When printing presses were introduced in Paris hundreds of years earlier, wielders of quill pens seized heavier weapons and marched on the enemy machines. And when an automatic loom was first operated in Danzig in 1661, the hand weavers of the town demanded that authorities suppress the invention, and themselves dragged the luckless inventor from his shop and drowned him.

Such setbacks were repeated in riots in England during 1812, when weavers smashed new automatic equipment. However, mechanical devices did come and stay. Automatic controls began to appear on more machines. In America the first entirely automatic mill went into operation on Red Clay Creek near Philadelphia in 1784. Built by Oliver Evans, this pioneer robot mill delivered a product untouched by human hands, using power furnished by water-driven paddlewheels.

In 1801 Frederick III of Germany tried to get manufacturers to use the new "fire machines" invented by Watt and others to take the place of human energy. Reluctant manufacturers claimed that such "cast metal monsters" would not be a help, but instead that they would increase costs, eliminate competition, and thus hurt trade generally. By 1842,

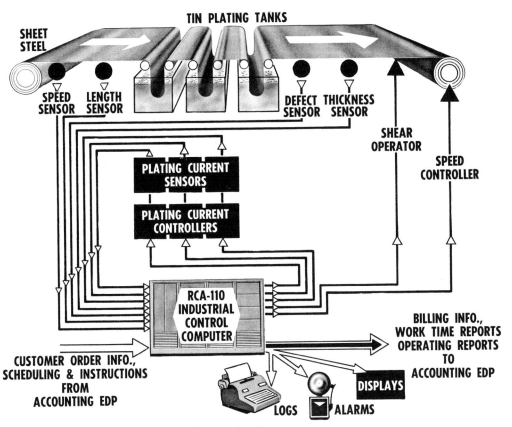

Automated, computer-controlled steel mill.   *Radio Corporation of America*

however, an estimated half-million machines were at work in the weaving trade alone, doing the work of seventeen million weavers! Little wonder that men fought against such job-stealing menaces.

Author Capek wrote his play *R.U.R.* in 1920, the same year that a man named A. O. Smith set up an automatic factory in the United States for producing auto chassis. This factory turned out a year's former supply of parts in just six months. Seven years later the communications industry turned its efforts toward automatic production with a system called Televox in which telephone signals activated remotely controlled machines in factories. Aided by such modern technology, the industrial revolution began to gather momentum.

GIANT STEPS

In the 1940's developments took place which hastened the robot boom. The mechanical "hand-arm" was developed to a high degree, and, even more important, the robot acquired a "brain." In 1946, the first electronic computer was completed and put into operation. The joining of these two components, the order-giving computer and the order-taking hand-arm, resulted in such a revolutionary robot that *Fortune* magazine published an article stating "the human machine-tender is at best a makeshift."

One result of this new robot was a new wave of scare stories with mechanical monsters taking over the world from helpless men. More intelligent was the development of the science of "automation." In 1946, the year of the first electronic computer, a Ford Motor Company engineer named D. S. Harder coined the new word, and in 1947 Ford formed its first automation department. The truly automatic factory was on its way.

Still another important development in the 1940's was the science of "cybernetics." Introduced by Norbert Wiener of Massachusetts Institute of Technology and Arturo Rosenblueth of Harvard, cybernetics is concerned with communication and control, not only in machines but in animals as well. Cybernetics comes from the Greek *kybernetes*, for steersman or governor; and this science and a more recent development called "bionics," the study of living systems as an aid in designing better artificial ones, show the parallels between biological and mechanical man.

The robot, then, is no new invention but a device that had its beginnings in the myth and legend of antiquity. Starting as an idea based on superstition and magic, it slowly became a reality, at first as an interesting toy and later as a crude substitute for human workers. The coming of modern technology has speeded the development of better robots, and the awkward mechanical man of the industrial revolution has evolved with electricity and electronics into a useful helper.

3
How the Robot Works

To learn how robots work let us first consider what the robot is designed to do. In the play *R.U.R.* the name means "worker," and the robots took over in factories and offices. Five hundred thousand of them were sent to the pampas of Argentina to grow corn—to relieve men of the drudgery of hard work and to reduce the cost of food and other needs. These were fictional robots, to be sure, but real robots are built for the same purpose: to do useful work. They are designed to do the work of humans, and to do it automatically.

Doing such work requires three things: *energy, muscles, control.* Just as we must eat and drink to provide our bodies with energy, so robots must be powered. They must have "limbs," or other parts to do the work. And they must have a "brain" to tell these limbs what to do.

Robots can be powered by springs, combustion engines, or electricity. Their parts are of metal, plastic, and other materials, in the form of motors, solenoids, relays, switches, levers, gears, springs, etc. The robot's brain can be a simple clockwork or a complex electronic computer. The simplest kind of robot is one that "does what it's wound up to do."

WIND-UP ROBOTS

There are many ways to tell time. Animals seem to do it instinctively, and humans can often wake themselves exactly at the hour they wish to. Some men claim to tell time by feeling the length of their whiskers. Of course it is the movement of the celestial bodies in the sky that measures time, and the ancients learned that they could mark the passage of time by observing sun or stars.

For many reasons—such as cloudy weather, poor eyesight, laziness, and so on—men of olden times learned to use mechanical devices for keeping time. Instead of squinting at stars or measuring the length of a shadow, clever inventors built primitive clocks in which dripping water, burning candles, or other fairly constant processes measured the passage of time. Finally the spring-driven clock with accurate gears and escapement was developed.

A clock is a fine machine. When we wind it up it behaves like the character Tik-Tok: it does just what we want it to do. Early robots were based on the wind-up idea, and they did the same thing each time they were wound up. The traffic light in its simplest form is a clockwork robot. Happily, the robot had a much more interesting future than such rigidly monotonous activity. Its possibilities were hinted at by the same ancients who built water clocks and still thought of the earth as the center of the universe. To impress their people, clever priests made temple doors open automatically at the rising of the sun. A crude system of mirrors, levers, pistons, and steam power accomplished this "magic." As the

sun reached the proper place in the sky, its rays were fo-
cused to boil water in a container: the resulting steam
pushed a piston that operated levers to open the door. Here
was a robot that could receive a signal from the outside
world and act upon that signal—the germ of true automatic
control for robots. Many centuries passed before such control was harnessed in a practical fashion.

FEEDBACK

We have already mentioned a principle very important to
the robot. This principle is called "feedback," and it is older
than any man-made machine. Living things depend on feedback for many of their actions. Basically, feedback consists of
trial and error, or punishment and reward. A child learns
through feedback—by trying various things that may or may
not be proper behavior. If his action gets him what he wants,
he behaves that way again.

We rely on physical principles every day without thinking
of them, and feedback is one of these. Our bodies operate
with this mechanism: when you reach for a piece of candy,
or lift a bottle of soda pop to your mouth, tiny signals are
sent from eye to brain to arm and back again. Has the arm
moved far enough, are the fingers opened properly? The result is a smooth, easy movement we scarcely appreciate for
the miracle it is.

Although man himself depends on feedback, it was many
centuries before he applied the feedback idea to machines
to make them robots.

In 1706, when a windmill began to saw wood in England,

a mob destroyed it. Despite such troubles, windmills continued to be built and were among the first machines to use feedback. Some of these great mills were so heavy that heading them into the wind was a hard job. But a smart man found a better way—an automatic way: he mounted a smaller windmill at right angles to the main windmill. As long as the windmill faced in the proper direction, the small blades remained motionless; but as soon as the windmill shifted, even slightly, the small blades caught some wind and started to turn. In doing so, they turned gears connected to a central hub, and soon the big windmill itself was again facing in the proper direction. This was the basic principle of feedback: when the wrong thing happened, it caused a correcting force to be generated. Wind from the wrong direction turned the mills to face the proper way.

The windmill did not develop into a machine of primary importance to modern civilization, but the feedback principle was soon adopted for other machines that did become most important. One of these was the steam engine.

The first practical steam engines were invented in an attempt to replace the horse. In the mines of England water was removed by horses working pumps. When it was said that a pump had so many "horsepower," that was exactly what the term meant. Thomas Newcomen, a metal parts dealer who often visited these mines on business, realized the expense involved in the horse-powered pumps. Newcomen resolved to develop a "fire-machine" that would turn the horse out to pasture, or at least free him for other work. By 1712 the inventor had succeeded, but his engine was soon to be improved.

THE ROBOTS ARE HERE

A youth named Humphrey Potter had been hired by New-comen to tend his mechanical monster as it pumped water. Young Potter didn't want to do a bit more dull work than he had to, and he soon tired of his task—which was simply moving a lever to admit steam into the cylinder of Newcomen's engine, and then moving it back to let the piston drop and thus pump water. All day long it was move the lever one way, let steam in; move it back and stop the flow of steam. Potter hit on the idea of tying the lever to the piston of the steam engine itself in such a way that the movement of the piston moved the steam lever! Now the engine worked even better than when Potter had been tending it, since the lever moved precisely when the steam valve should operate, and not when Potter happened to move it. The young man had invented the slide valve (still used on some steam engines)., which was adopted by James Watt when he patented his more advanced rotating engine in 1769.

Watt went on to do much more than this. He had inherited from Newcomen an engine that ran itself, to be sure, but one that might run too fast or too slow. Watt wanted to control his engine so that it would run at any speed desired, even with fluctuations in steam pressure, and changing loads. His solution was feedback by means of the flyball governor, a simple system of weights spinning on a shaft driven by the engine. A similar arrangement was already in use in flour mills, but Watt first used it with steam engines. The faster the engine ran, the higher the centrifugal force pushed the weights. And the higher the weights, the more they closed off the steam valve. If the engine ran too slowly the governor admitted more steam. The governor thus adjusted the speed anywhere within the engine's range.

Now the windmill feedback idea had been put to more widespread use, and feedback in the factory became an important principle in the industrial revolution. However, its use was not limited to robots in performing industrial chores. Before long it was also put to good use in robot helmsmen on ships.

If there were no contrary winds, or ocean currents, or other disturbing forces, sailing a ship from one place to another would be a fairly simple task. We would just find the correct direction to sail, and point ourselves that way. But mariners knew that sailing always meant tedious hours at the wheel to keep the ship headed in the right direction. Why not apply the feedback principle to the ship's compass and add a control system leading to the rudder? Even as a seaman's eyes detected that the ship's course did not coincide with the compass course, so the robot "automatic pilot" might detect the error and apply a correction.

Of course the robot helmsman had to be trained in his

Airborne computer is robot navigator for high-speed airplanes, missiles, or space vehicles.   *Librascope Division, General Precision, Inc.*

task. Just as an apprentice seaman might allow his ship to wander across the sea, so the automatic pilot might not sail a true course at first. It might make many quick and violent corrections, or let the ship drift too far before swinging it back to the proper course. Either of these extremes was undesirable, and it took proper adjustment of the robot to make it sail like a good mariner. But once adjusted, the robot could then do a better job than the man it replaced—a smooth, tireless, and error-free job. Only when violent seas beset the ship would a human have to stand by ready to apply an extraordinary correction that the autopilot was not prepared to deliver.

The robot that steers ships is a wonderful mechanism; another that flies today's high-speed aircraft is far more advanced and amazing. The automatic pilot today uses radar eyes that see through hundreds of miles of darkness, optical eyes that "shoot" the stars, and an electronic brain that performs thousands of mathematical operations accurately in the wink of a human eye.

FEEDBACK CLOSER TO HOME

Control engineers use a term called "closing the loop." Without robot feedback, human intervention is required to change the output of a machine. This situation is called an "open loop." We are familiar with this right in our homes. Suppose we have a furnace that is not equipped with automatic controls. Once turned on, the furnace will produce heat until some outside force turns it off. We are that force. When it becomes too hot for comfort, we turn off the furnace.

When it is too cold, we turn it back on. This is called closing the loop, and it is another way of describing feedback.

Today a robot called a thermostat puts feedback to work and does the job of regulating the temperature in our homes. We sense heat with nerve endings in our skin. The thermostat senses temperature with a metal element that expands when heated and contracts when cooled. At a certain temperature the movement of this element operates a switch that controls the furnace. If the furnace burns oil, the level of this fuel is regulated by a float valve that also uses the feedback principle. If the fuel level gets too high, the valve shuts off. If fuel is low, the valve opens and lets in more.

Some traffic signals have become feedback robots too. They change the lengths of their red and green signals to match the amount of traffic by using photocell eyes or roadway switches to count the cars. Some can turn all their signal lights red when they receive a radio warning from an approaching fire engine or police car.

ELECTRONIC AGE ROBOTS

We should keep in mind one important point about robots or thinking machines, and what they can and cannot do. It has been truly said that we get no more out of any machine than we put into it. Otherwise we would be violating basic scientific laws and venturing into the field of magic. Only in fiction do magic things happen; real robots must have proper input to deliver desired output.

Early robots depended entirely on mechanical principles for their operation. Jacquard's punched cards admitted need-

THE ROBOTS ARE HERE

les through the proper holes; Watt's governor worked because of weight and centrifugal force. Electricity has now come into the picture, followed by the greater marvel of electronics. Along with the temperature-sensing thermostat we now have accurate pressure and humidity sensors. We have

Example of logic the robot is capable of.

Radio Corporation of America

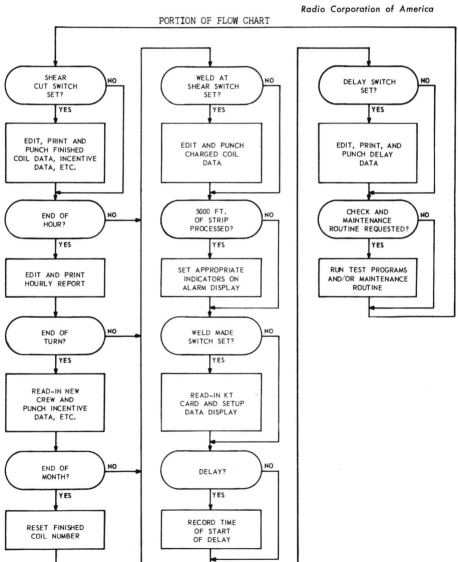

PORTION OF FLOW CHART

devices that "see" with photocells, or "hear" with microphones. Since the invention of the printing press, the machine has been able to write. More recently it has added reading to its talents.

Today's robot can remember. More important, its brain can analyze given information and reach a logical conclusion. "Logic" circuits are built into the electronic brain, so that it can do more than add numbers. It can make decisions in a split second and order its robot arms, legs, or voice to carry out those decisions. It is actually beginning to "think," as we shall see later on.

The new robots can see or hear for great distances with the help of electronics. Working with "fellow" robots many miles away, they can pass information on almost instantaneously. Russia has factories controlled by robots hundreds of miles away. Here in America widely separated industrial plants are linked and controlled by remote robot systems.

There are hundreds of different kinds of robots today, ranging from simple ones like automatic toasters to complex air traffic control systems. We should remember that all these robots are basically the same. They have the three essentials needed for doing useful work. They must have power, they must have limbs or other active parts, and they must have some kind of a control system if they are to be more than an ordinary machine. Above all, we should be aware that there is no magic to robots. For their output they depend on an input. Since man provides that input, man, not the robot, is potentially dangerous in a world of robots. There are no evil robots; only evil men.

4

Robot Roll Call

We have thermostat, clock, elevator, and traffic light robots by the hundreds of thousands serving us, but other robots do still more interesting things. Only a few years ago if you had tried to buy a robot you would have been asked if you were joking, but today you can order industrial robots by the dozen—if you have the money to pay for them, of course! We have already mentioned the dues-paying mechanical men. Called "TransfeRobots," they sell for about twenty-five thousand dollars, ready to go to work. TransfeRobot is an assembly-line worker that feeds presses, loads or unloads assembly lines, sorts, packages, assembles, welds, rivets, glues, bends or caps as required. A variety of attachments are available, and the robot works at speeds of up to fifty operations a minute.

Although you would never mistake TransfeRobot for a movie mechanical man, it does have an electronic brain, an arm, a wrist, and fingers or jaws. This robot can pick up a part, position it accurately and quickly in a trimming press, tell the press to cut off excess material, and then remove the finished part. On a clock assembly line, the robot oils eight bearings at a time. In addition to giving orders to other machines, it can also signal other TransfeRobots working on the assembly line. And if trouble occurs the robot just quits work and calls for help by flashing a red light at the human fore-

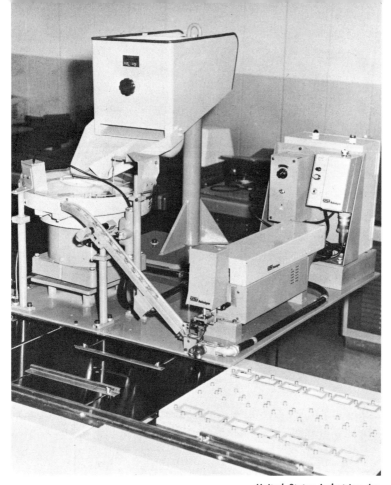

This TransfeRobot "sees" color differences and properly positions packages of gum.

man. Recently this assembly line worker has acquired eyes and can distinguish colors. One job that uses its new ability is positioning packages of gum for display board mounting.

A robot called "Unimate" is a grown-up cousin of TransfeRobot and it can handle really *big* jobs. The smaller machine has a reach of just ten inches, but Unimate's long arm can reach from the floor to a height of more than seven feet. Like TransfeRobot, Unimate can be taught to do many different jobs instead of just one. Its brain can memorize two hundred separate steps, and the way it learns is interesting and simple. The boss leads the robot by the hand, as it were, through the new task, closing its big fingers, moving its arm the proper distance, opening its fingers again, and so on. As this is done, magnetic switches in the "memory" of the robot are set. One practice run is all Unimate needs, and it is then ready to work alone with never an error. When the time comes to do another task, the boss just erases the memory from Unimate's brain by pushing a button to demagnetize the switches, and teaches it the new job. Few human employees are as quick to learn—and the robot has other advantages too.

In one factory operation, Unimate lifts heavy metal cylinders that have been heated to 1600° F. It can weld or grind metal with no need for goggles, and it paints with a

"Unimate" showing off its muscles and its brain.

Unimation, Inc.

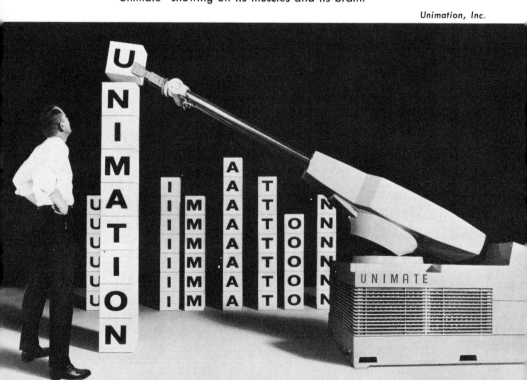

"Fleximan" being the perfect host. Will such machines be the servants of the future?

spray gun with no danger of choking on fumes. If necessary the robot can work twenty-four hours a day without getting tired.

Besides being able to communicate with associated equipment, Unimate can also teach other robots the job it has learned, relaying the information electronically to Unimates in another plant if desired. Thus it is necessary to teach only one robot a job to have a whole battery of them go to work on it.

Another new robot is called "Fleximan." It is similar in operation to TransfeRobot and Unimate, and it is available in four sizes for handling objects weighing from one and a half pounds. The largest has a reach of six feet. Fleximan handles work with mechanical fingers, or with vacuum or magnetic pick-ups. It can be mounted on wheels if necessary.

Generally we think of robots as mechanical men, but some

THE ROBOTS ARE HERE

Computer Division, General Electric Company

Robot bank clerk processes 750 checks per minute.

of them are taking over jobs traditionally done by women. A typical example is ERMA, whose initials stand for Electronic Recording Method of Accounting. Created to help keep us from drowning in a sea of paperwork, ERMA works for the Bank of America in California. It is perhaps the biggest bank clerk in the world, and needs about ten thousand square feet of floor space. ERMA sorts, posts, and records one hundred and ten thousand bank accounts in less than three and a half hours—more than twice as many in a *minute* as the human clerk can do in an *hour*.

ERMA and its robot cousins across the country make occasional mistakes in which a delighted bank customer may be credited with a million-dollar deposit. But in most of these cases some human helper is really to blame, for ERMA can work all night without getting tired or careless. It reads with magnetic or photoelectric eyes, thinks with a high-speed electronic brain, and writes with a printer that dashes off nine-hundred lines a minute.

Robot stenographers such as "Robotype" and "Flexowriter" type hundreds of letters a day using a punched-paper-tape memory. Robot typesetters automatically "justify" lines of type, so that the margins on both sides are even. This is a task that once required a highly skilled human typesetter. Other robots are now learning to proofread copy for errors in spelling, and even to hyphenate words properly.

ROBOT "ANIMALS"

Edmund C. Berkeley, an expert on computers, and the publisher of a journal in that field, has long been interested in robots and has built some of the most interesting of the smaller types. Because of Mr. Berkeley's work with computers and mathematics, it is natural that many of his robots have been directed toward the solving of problems. Among these were "Simon," an electromechanical robot that "knew" four things and gave answers by blinking his eyes; and "Geniac" and "Relay Moe," game-playing robots.

In 1951 Berkeley built a mechanical squirrel he called "Squee." This sixteen-pound robot was twenty-one inches long and rolled about looking for nuts. Battery powered, Squee searched methodically for its prize, using two photocell eyes. When located, the nut was scooped up and carried proudly to the nest and then Squee set out to find more! The robot's brain consisted of a dozen relays and electronic tubes.

THE ROBOTS ARE HERE

Across the Atlantic, neurophysiologist Dr. W. Grey Walter of England's Burden Institute constructed some fascinating animal-like robots. In his study of the operation of living brains, Dr. Walter built electromechanical "tortoises." The first, like Squee, rolled about on battery power, guided by photocell eyes. They avoided obstacles set in their way and returned to their cave and "fed" themselves from the electric outlet when their batteries ran down.

The robots did all this on only two "brain cells." Dr. Walter later built another robot called CORA which could do much more than its forerunners. CORA had the ability to learn, while ELMER and ELSIE never improved on the little intelligence they began "life" with. CORA stands for Conditioned Reflex Analog. It responded to whistles, and learned from being tapped on its shell not to do certain things.

Machina speculatrix negotiates an obstacle.

Dr. W. Grey Walter

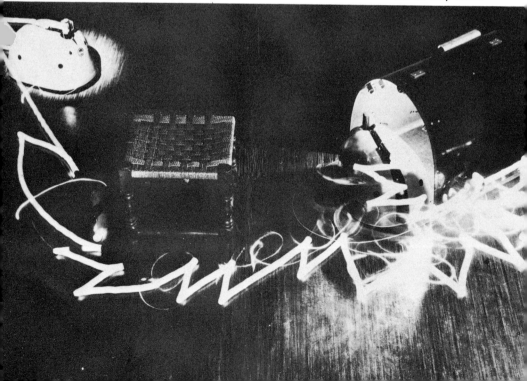

Bell Telephone Laboratories
Dr. Claude Shannon with his mechanical mouse, "Theseus."

Scientists have used mice in their studies for years. One of the most amazing is "Theseus," an electromechanical robot mouse created by Dr. Claude Shannon of Bell Telephone Laboratories. Many years ago on that same island of Crete where Talos, the robot defender, patrolled daily, the Athenian hero Theseus succeeded in slaying the Minotaur. Among Theseus' adventures was that of negotiating the tortuous labyrinth, or maze, of Crete, and he did this by marking his trail with a thread. Dr. Shannon named his mouse Theseus after the mythical Greek because the mouse too was expert at running a maze. Instead of a thread it used an artificial brain of electric relays to "remember" the right turns.

The mouse maze consisted of twenty-five squares and

Bell Telephone Laboratories

Light on, robot mouse traces first run through maze (left) and perfect second run taking only fifteen seconds (right).

movable partitions that could be set up to make millions of paths from start to "cheese," as Dr. Shannon called the finish. On its initial run, Theseus was faced with four choices in each square. It could go straight ahead, turn right, turn left, or go back the way it came. Much like an ordinary mouse the robot blundered hit and miss through the maze the first time, taking about two minutes. But once having "learned" the way by setting the relays correctly at each turn, it could run the maze perfectly in just a few seconds. Theseus was used primarily for developing more efficient telephone switching circuits—the only mechanical mouse ever to work for the telephone company!

EDUCATED ROBOTS

We find robots of all shapes and sizes, from a tiny electronic mathematician known as "Shoebox" because of its shape, to the giant air defense robot called SAGE. Shoebox is much smarter than its name implies for not only does it do arithmetic problems accurately, it does them on voice commands from its human builders. SAGE, at the other extreme, includes not one brain, but dozens of them, plus eyes, ears, and voices that cover the country. Its name stands for Semi-Automatic Ground Environment. SAGE still needs much human help to do its job of controlling our air defenses.

Teaching machines are being used ever more widely, and many of these are robot systems. Examples of these mechanical professors are "Auto Tutor" and "Didak" which impart programmed learning to students. More complex than simple tutoring machines are ambitious robot teachers like CLASS, designed by the firm that designed SAGE. CLASS stands for Computer-based Laboratory for Automated School Systems and can teach many students individually and simultaneously, varying the material presented to fit the student's learning rate. When CLASS has finished teaching for the day it can take over routine clerical jobs on a night shift.

Another robot teacher called PLATO for "Programmed Logic for Automatic Teaching Operations" has been developed. This impressively named machine teaches, coaches, tests, and even tattles if the student is idle.

An electronic brain named ILLIAC (Illinois Automatic

THE ROBOTS ARE HERE

Dr. W. Grey Walter

Two robots of the species *machina speculatrix* that see, remember, and move about without striking obstacles.

Computer) has composed music, including "Illiac Suite for String Quartet"; and a German travel agency robot named ZUSE plans tours for its clients. The trend toward robots doing so many things has prompted some interesting science-fiction stories. In one, future generations of robot-powered humans accidentally "discover" that man himself can control a vehicle! In another, a race of robots in a world that no longer has any humans does biological research and learns how to create man, the "human robot."

These are some of the robots inhabiting today's world and giving us a hint of those that will be the next generation. In this do-it-yourself era it is quite possible to add to the robot population with a mechanical man of your own. While a mechanical pet as smart as Dr. Walter's CORA, or even ELMER or Squee is beyond the mechanical and electronic ability of most of us, simpler robots have been built by hobbyists and science students. Such projects are excellent for science fairs, class projects, and so on. A study of back issues of popular mechanical and electronic magazines will yield a variety of easy-to-build robots.

5
Robots at Work

We would probably miss many robots in our search for them because at first glance they don't look like mechanical men at all. Automation, for instance, is sometimes called the "invisible robot." But looks are deceiving and the hard-to-recognize robots are among the most important of our mechanical and electronic helpers.

It will be helpful at this point to remember what a robot is supposed to do: a useful task of some sort. We should keep in mind also that doing a man's job does not necessarily mean that the robot must look like a man.

ROBOTS IN OUR HOMES

There are modern counterparts of Ali Baba's automatic door opener in many homes whose fortunate owners don't have to get out of their automobiles to open or shut the garage doors: a radio transmitter in the car sends a signal, and an unseen robot opens the door. Or perhaps a robot eye takes the place of the electronic ear.

Now that we've driven into the garage and heard the automated door swing smoothly shut, let's look for more of these robots who don't look the part. One in the corner of the laundry room is called an automatic water heater. Once upon a time we heated water over a fire, checking the temperature now and then with our fingers. The robot water heater han-

42

dles this chore for us twenty-four hours a day to keep the water at just the temperature we want.

Some of this water goes just a short distance to another robot—the automatic washer. Humans used to scrub clothes by hand. But even with an invention known as the washboard this wasn't a popular task, and today most homes have automatic washers. The washer has another robot partner that dries the clothes to make life even easier. With electromechanical brains and muscle power, robot laundries do a better job on our clothes than the humans they replace. Few women challenge this statement because they are pleased to be free for more interesting activities.

Some of us have another robot doing the dishes. This helper uses water far hotter than we could put our hands into, and it dries the dishes too. Another robot tends our toast and pops it up just the way we like it. A robot oven cooks the meals. A radio robot wakes us up in the morning to the sound of music and the smell of coffee brewing. This same robot will turn off the radio at night after we are asleep. While we're about it let's not forget the automatic record player, a pretty clever robot also.

The air-conditioning control is a handy robot who works as janitor around the clock for seven days a week. Other robots do chores like sprinkling the lawn automatically, and a robot gardener that mows the lawn unattended is in the experimental stage!

OFFICE ROBOTS

The robots in our homes provide just a hint of what we

find when we look into the business world. Many buildings have automatic door openers. Robot elevators still awe some of the more timid of us as they purr about their business with mechanical efficiency. If we use a little imagination it is easy to picture the building itself as a huge robot breathing in fresh air, winking its many eyes, and warming or cooling itself as the weather changes. Automatic sprinklers put out fires. Windows and doors may be automatically opened, closed, or locked. In some buildings there is no need for janitors to make their rounds. A central control room constantly monitors temperature throughout the building, draws drapes, and guards entrances. An automatic telephone switchboard handles the many communications between this building and others half way around the world.

Once we've accustomed ourselves to the idea of buildings as robots let's tackle an even bigger concept—that of the business robot. We have mentioned the banking robot ERMA whose handwriting is on most checks these days. It's a special handwriting that enables robots to handle the billions of checks Americans write each year. The robot is freeing humans from a life of "making marks on paper," a chore that makes up a good part of business.

Too big to look like robots in the usual sense, automated business systems are moving from banks to the stock market, warehouses, supermarkets, airlines, and railroad operation; to name just a few of their applications. But even these broad fields are not the best examples of automation today.

ROBOTS AND AUTOMATION

Since automation is defined as the substitution of artificial devices for human organs of observation, decision, and effort, we may expect to find robots busily at work in our factories. In our roll call of robots we met several assembly-line robots including TransfeRobot, Unimate, and Fleximan, but these and the many other machines like them are only tiny individual parts of the robot giant called automation.

The methods of the 1920's seem childishly simple when compared with the technique of automation introduced in 1946. In the early days of mass production, machines took over for human muscles, but man himself had to stay right on the scene to see that the machines did their jobs properly. Today, however, the human supervisor may be in an office out of sight of the automatic machine that works smoothly and tirelessly by itself.

While these individual robots go about their specific tasks, the larger robot of total automation concerns itself with the whole picture of production. Robot planners in an auto factory decide how many carloads of steel must roll through the gates, when and in what quantities other materials are needed, how many deluxe model cars should be built in a given week, and where the finished cars are to be shipped when they roll out the door a mile down the line. Years ago Samuel Butler wrote a satire describing human workers as parasitical to machines, men who served only to oil and otherwise tend the engines. Today this state of affairs seems to be coming about—where robot machines once aided man, now man aids the robot, when and if it needs help.

ROBOT RESEARCHER

A robot librarian sounds like a stunt, but we may some

Robot librarian may be the key to solving the problem of information retrieval.

day see such an automation of books and other material that robots will *be* the library. Along with our population explosion we have another known as the information explosion. In the field of technical literature alone it is estimated that each day enough new material is written to fill a complete set of the *Encyclopaedia Britannica*. While it is nice to know that scientists are so diligent, much of this information is not readily available to those who might make good use of it. Instead, much of it is lost in continuously accumulating tons of paperwork, and may never do more than gather dust on a library shelf.

This sad truth became known when science and industry spent fortunes solving various problems before learning that someone else had already done the work. Cynics call this "spending our lives reinventing the wheel" and it is, of course, a great waste of valuable time and money. Yet an authority said recently that even if solving a particular problem cost a hundred-thousand dollars, it would be cheaper than the research that might turn up a previous solution.

What is needed is more effective storage of information and a means of quickly searching through it to find the items of interest. Robots are already at work on the problem with their electronic brains. Reading machines prepare "abstracts," brief descriptions of articles, and file them away in computer memories. Other robots can search through catalogs of this stored information at lightning speed to find the right material. In tests the robots have been found not only faster but more exact than human researchers, never missing a word because they are tired or angry or have poor eyesight.

Robot translators also make information retrieval—and many other jobs, too—far easier. Most of them handle printed

Robot teaching machine can be programmed to teach many different subjects. *United States Industries, Inc.*

material but some are now tackling the tougher job of translating spoken words.

The automated library, linked by telephone or radio to other libraries across the country and even around the world, will benefit scientist, scholar, and casual reader as well. A recent project involves the printing of a book by computer, fed by radio signals bounced from communication satellites like " telstar." It is thought that this can be done in just a few minutes, no matter how far away the wanted book is, and at a cost of only about $2.50, or less than the price of the original volume. The robot library may place the literary wealth of the world at our finger tips.

The legal field also benefits greatly from such an automated information retrieval system. Instead of a lawyer spending tedious hours poring over law books for precedents, the electronic brain takes over this task and even helps prepare the legal brief.

A group of lawyers has suggested a robot that will predict the decisions of the Supreme Court simply by searching its electronic memory for applicable laws and weighing past judgments of the Court. If a machine can do this, it might be asked why have a human court at all? This is a controversial question, to be sure, for no one wants only the hard, cold facts from a robot instead of the more human idea of tempering justice with mercy. But with our courts jammed with a backlog of cases that increases each year, perhaps robot assistants to lawyers and judges can help streamline proceedings and create a more efficient system.

ROBOTS AT WORK

ROBOTS IN THE WHITE HOUSE

Ours is a government of the people, for the people, and by the people, but it is aided by the robots of automation. In fact, the government helped pioneer the field way back in the 1880's by adopting machines for compiling the census. These crude early counters have been replaced by faster electronic brains.

One robot greeted with mixed emotions was the electronic tax-collector, but we should be glad to have this machine that will help us to be honest. The Internal Revenue Department began using electronic brains in 1960 and soon all accounts will be handled in this way. Instead of being kept in folders in file cabinets, our records go onto miles of tape "memories" and the machine can sort these in seconds to double-check our tax statements.

There are so many millions of Americans with Social Security records that only with automation can everything be kept straight. And the post office is adding new robot mail-handling systems as fast as it can to keep from drowning in an ocean of mail. Robot printers address mail for many customers, including magazine publishers and mail-order houses. In post offices reading machines scan mail at high speed and sort it for routing to the proper location. Of course, some sacrifices have to be made to gain the benefits of robot mail clerks, and recently the request went out for the public to stop enclosing the tops cut from cans and similar objects in letters!

Increasing population and more paperwork are bursting

Military Products Group, Minneapolis-Honeywell Regulator Co.
Robot war machine for mock sea battles. Next step would be to let
robots fight the real wars!

the seams of many other organizations that help run our
country. Domestic programs, and foreign relations as well,
are becoming so complex and involve so many important factors that it is inevitable for them to need more and more
help from robots. This is particularly true in the Defense Department, where electronic computers are fighting their first
battles—including some against old-line admirals and gen-
erals who can't see eye to eye with robots!

Robots range from tiny thermostats to complete steel mills,

from banking systems to complexes of factories. They have come into being for one reason only: they are needed if our increasing population is to maintain its living standards.

Artists have fancifully drawn factories with cavernous mouths that eat up raw material, noses that blow smoke, and powerful arms that forge the finished products man needs. If we think about it a bit, we may decide that such drawings aren't too fanciful at that. At the same time, we can see that the same caricature might well apply to banks, libraries, schools, and even to the White House. Surely, and quite rapidly, the robots are automating the world.

Computer control of steel-making operations at Jones and Laughlin.

Computer Division, General Electric Co.

6

Mobot, the Robot on a String

We have mentioned the chess-playing robot operated by a hidden assistant who pulled and pushed the right levers. Although the Von Kempelen machine did not play fair, it does demonstrate a certain kind of robot—a sort of robot on a string.

A simpler example is the marionette, the lifelike doll dangling from strings and made to perform in a very realistic fashion by a clever human being. Today a special breed of robot is something like the marionette. It is the "Mobot," or manipulated robot. Although Mobots have performed to entertain an audience, they are not used to trick people as the turbanned chess player did. Instead they are built to do useful work of a very special and dangerous kind.

If you've watched a blasting crew in action, you may have seen them use a detonator to set off a large charge of dynamite from a safe distance. The detonator permits a man several hundred feet away to close the switch that fires the charge. Launching a rocket is in the same category and calls for a remote-control technique. The Mobot is based on the need for such "operation at a distance," and it was developed to its present state largely because of the most deadly explosive of all—nuclear energy.

MOBOT, THE ROBOT ON A STRING

THE ROBOT AND THE ATOM

During World War II it was rumored that "top secret" robots were at work in our nuclear research centers because of the deadly hazards there. It wasn't just the explosive force of the bomb that was dangerous, although surely that effect was bad enough. Another danger was radiation.

When the Curies discovered the radioactive elements radium and polonium, they also discovered that radioactivity, the emission of high-energy radiation as these elements disintegrated, could kill. Some early researchers died of exposure, suffering from a terrible new kind of sickness. Workers died or were terribly injured by radiation in industry.

Preparing atomic material for a bomb or creating an

"Mobots" shown in artist's concepts, working with hot metal castings on assembly line, and repairing an undersea cable.

Hughes Aircraft Co.

atomic pile for industrial power generation demands protective measures if the humans involved are to survive. The best protection against radiation is lead, the soft metal that effectively soaks up deadly rays. Special leaded glass in very thick sheets also affords protection. But if a man were to build himself a suit of lead and glass he would collapse in a heap under the ponderous weight of his "armor." So the remote manipulator robot with flexible arms and powerful fingers went to work in atom research centers.

At first these robots were fixed in one spot, able to work only within reach of their arms and guided awkwardly by men behind thick, leaded-glass windows. But slowly they acquired television eyes, microphone ears, and other sensing organs to monitor temperature and radiation. Mobots have been mounted on wheels so that they can be driven and steered about their tasks. Operated by humans at control panels fitted with levers and foot pedals, their strong fingers pick up heavy blocks or rods and move them about accurately and safely.

In some respects the Mobot resembles industrial robots like TransfeRobot and Unimate. Hands and arms, for example, are much alike in each case, but the "brain" is different. While the industrial robots are controlled by their own electronic brains, Mobots are operated by human brains. Hughes Aircraft Company, which coined the name Mobot, points out that it is possible to add an artificial brain to a Mobot if desired, complete with a tape "memory" so that once it has been taught a task by its human instructor it can repeat on its own. But Mobots are usually intended to operate much like the toy robots we control with pushbuttons, or even by

MOBOT, THE ROBOT ON A STRING

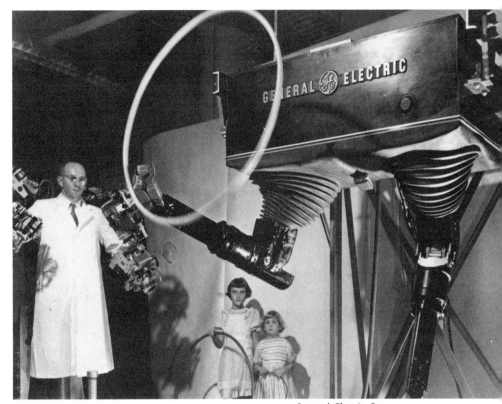

General Electric Co.

"Handyman" robot demonstrates its versatility by twirling hula hoop.

voice commands through a flexible electrical cable.

As a worker in dangerous environments the Mobot was successful from the start. Human operators got the "feel" of its arms and fingers, and soon their robot charges were able to perform with amazing manual dexterity. They pour dangerous chemicals from one beaker to another, handle radioactive materials, and do other important tasks that man would have to risk his own safety to duplicate.

Manipulator robots did many other things for publicity. There were, as usual, pictures taken with pretty girls— "Beauty and the Beast" themes. They twirled hula hoops, bent iron bars, and even zipped zippers. But there was serious work too, and one serious job was that of aircraft mechanic.

Atomic energy proved useful for producing electrical power for industry and utilities, and it was inevitable that this source of power be used in submarines and surface ships. Airplanes, however, represent more of a challenge because a plane must be built of lighter material than a ship, and there is some radiation hazard connected with the operation of nuclear aircraft. The crew can be shielded, but it is difficult to protect the mechanic who must check and even work on the reactors that drive the aircraft. The answer was "Handyman," built by General Electric for the Air Force and the Atomic Energy Commission.

Handyman, designed to serve as master mechanic on atom-powered planes, is well-named. Where earlier Mobots had simple metal fingers, Handyman simulates the action of human hands that fold and unfold. There are ten basic motions built into Handyman's arms and hands. As a result it can use a screwdriver, tighten or loosen bolts, and do other tasks a mechanic is called on to perform. With giant arms that span nine feet from fingertip to fingertip, Handyman has tremendous strength, yet it can delicately pluck the petals from a flower.

One of Handyman's descendants is surely the largest individual robot in the world. This eighty-five ton giant is named "Beetle," and it too was built for the Air Force. Beetle is so heavy that it rides on tank treads to keep from bogging down in soft ground. Towering twenty-five feet tall, it has arms sixteen feet long, and can punch holes through concrete walls! Yet it too is gentle when necessary and can pick up an egg without crushing the shell. Beetle is designed to work on NASA's Project Rover, a nuclear rocket development program. This will involve not only radiation hazards but

The Air Force robot, "Beetle," an eighty-five ton giant for working in dangerous nuclear environments.   *General Electric Co.*

also extremely delicate assembly operations. So Beetle uses hand or power tools and even handles a television camera when necessary.

A 500-horsepower engine powers Beetle with a 110-horsepower auxiliary unit for lights and communication. Its nervous system contains about four-hundred *miles* of wires! Though Beetle is designed to do construction and maintenance work on the Rover project, it can function as a rescue worker as well in case something goes amiss.

Instead of controlling the machine from some distance away, Beetle's human master sits right in the robot's cab. This enormous "skull" is shielded with lead a foot thick and leaded glass two feet thick, and as a result it weighs fifty tons. Should even this protection be insufficient during direct exposure to a "hot" reactor, Beetle can see around corners by taking a television camera out of its pocket and pointing it into the area of interest with one of its sixteen-foot arms. In addition to being shielded from radiation, the operator is protected by a three-ton air-conditioning unit that keeps cab temperature in the mid-seventies even when it is 130° above zero, or 25° below outside.

One of the most dangerous jobs today is that of firefighting, where men are exposed to fire, falling material, asphyxiation, and electrical shock. The robot can withstand all these hazards. Perhaps we will soon see mechanical men taking over the most dangerous of the fireman's tasks. Already being constructed are robot aerial firefighters which will seek out a blaze and drop a bomb of chemicals on it. Such robot helicopters will look much like the DASH robot already built by Gyrodyne and used by the Navy for antisubmarine warfare. (See photograph, page 111.)

"WALKING" ROBOTS

In addition to Handyman and Beetle, General Electric is developing a different kind of robot. So far we have been concerned mainly with "manipulation," that is, with hand movements. But the new General Electric robot will be called a "pedipulator" because it walks much as a man.

Not the Air Force but the Army is interested in a walking robot, and foot soldiers can take consolation from the fact that future pedipulators may do some of their work for them. Designed for the Army's Boston Ordnance District, the walking machines will be for off-the-road locomotion. Instead of human-size limbs, they will have giant twelve-foot legs that can take seven-league strides over rough country.

Although agility and power for rough terrain are the main

"Walking" robot is called CAM, for Cybernetic Anthropomorphous Machine. *General Electric Co.*

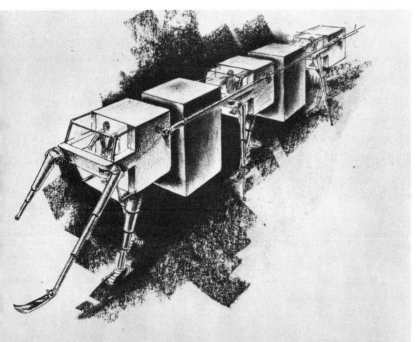

considerations of the Army, the walking machine is expected to jog along at a speedy thirty-five miles an hour, far faster than a human's three or four mile speed. But lest the infantryman think he is getting too big a break, it should be pointed out that he will operate the pedipulator himself. The walking machine will be able to walk on level or slightly sloping ground; it will be able to sidestep and to turn around and also to negotiate steps.

The pedipulator will also be fitted with arms of the Handyman or Beetle variety. The Army foresees this machine taking over such tasks as carrying supplies, fighting fires, rescue work, and even carrying litters of wounded or injured men.

ROBOT DIVERS

We have seen Mobot move out of the nuclear laboratory and into open country. It has also moved from dry land into the sea, and according to Dr. John W. Clark of Hughes Aircraft, it is under the water that this kind of robot will reach its greatest potential.

Dr. Clark reminds us that although the sea offers food, fuel, and many other materials we require in increasing quantities, thus far we are about as effective in our use of these as the American Indians were with their land resources before European colonization began. At that time the land supported something less than a million human beings; today we have one hundred and seventy million in the United States alone, with three hundred and fifty million predicted for the year 2000. We may have to harvest the sea to keep up with such growth, yet thus far we know less about the surface beneath our seas than we do about the moon!

There is a reason for this ignorance, and it is not a lack of interest on the part of our scientists and planners for the future. The reason is that the environment beneath the sea is in its way as hazardous for man as is that of the nuclear reactor. To give an example, when the bathysphere *Trieste* recently set a record by diving thirty-five thousand feet into the Marianas Trench in the Pacific, the pressure on the craft's hull was eight tons per square inch, compared with fifteen pounds at sea level. *Trieste* mounts a mechanical hand-arm much like those of the Mobots, for this is the only way a human can do any work against such pressure.

Science-fiction stories describe the horrible fate of men accidentally exposed to the hard vacuum of space. Pressure inside their bodies literally explodes them outward and they freeze in the process. Fortunately this has not yet happened to any of our astronauts who have ventured into the airless regions of space, and we hope it never will. But the reverse has happened many times under the sea, where the danger is not pressure from within the body, but pressure from the sea without. Deep-sea divers have been literally crammed into their steel helmets when air pressure from pumps on the surface failed. They have died from the "bends," an agonizing condition brought on by too-rapid ascent to the surface after a dive, which causes nitrogen to boil out of the blood and lodge in parts of the body.

Even skindivers, who cannot venture very far beneath the surface, have met disaster in a number of ways. They too can suffer from the bends. Some have become intoxicated on the oxygen they breathe and have lost control of their actions. Others have simply drowned, been trapped beneath the sea, or been killed by sharks or other fish. Perhaps one of the most agonizing deaths is that of the abalone or pearl diver who is caught by a giant shellfish and cannot free himself before his supply of air runs out.

The sea around us, then, is a potentially deadly enemy, even though it may have first nurtured life and today offers hope for feeding and otherwise providing for the increasing population of the dry-land world. In addition to the dangers from pressure and denizens of the deep, and the inconvenience of getting around in water, there is the difficulty of seeing anything in the darkness not far below the surface. Bright searchlights don't penetrate this murk very far, and undersea explorers find that the least movement on the sea bottom may churn up clouds of mud that persist for a long time.

Instead of sending man himself down to the dangers of the deep sea, why not send Mobots? We build submarine vessels that withstand pressure, and fit them with television eyes and sonar ears. Scientists and engineers thus work in comfort and safety thousands of feet above the Mobot diver, seeing what it sees, hearing what it hears, and exploring or working with its mechanical limbs.

Our Navy is concerned with underwater research, and one of the first of the underwater robots was built for it. Called RUM, for Remote Underwater Manipulator, this robot at the end of a cable has crawled about the bottom of the Pacific fitted with television and a hand-arm manipulator.

MOBOT, THE ROBOT ON A STRING

Scripps Institute of Oceanography

RUM, the Navy's ocean-going robot, wades into the sea.

RUM operated from the shore and moved on tank treads. It was built by the Scripps Institution of Oceanography at La Jolla, California.

Hughes Aircraft's answer to undersea exploration is a development of its landbased Mobot. Mobot takes well to the sea and its flexible arms have been called octopus-like. Unlike RUM, which must crawl on the bottom, Mobots are equipped with propellers that move them horizontally or vertically, and they can thus clear obstacles, descend vertically to an area of interest, and generally be more flexible in their operation.

Shell Oil Company was the first to put a Mobot to work as a "roughneck" that dives in two-hundred foot depths off

Robot preparing to dive for work on underwater oil well.

the California coast to drill wells. This Mobot did its first real underwater job off Santa Barbara County. Costing a quarter of a million dollars, the Mobot can swim to its work, seeing with television and hearing with sonar to find the oil well being drilled. While it can see about thirty feet with its television eyes, it has a range of fourteen hundred feet with sonar. Besides these senses, the Hughes Mobot has a gyro-compass to tell direction and a microphone to hear with. It handles a large socket wrench with its arm, and later models will use other tools as well.

Such success lends strength to suggestions that future Mobots will explore the ocean floor, operate mines there, and even farm the sea just as mechanical equipment harvests our land crops.

THE MAN-MACHINE LINK

While the first Mobots were kept on a short leash and always in sight of their human masters, the connections have become longer and longer, and electric wiring has given way to radio control. Radio and television take the place of ears and eyes, and man is able to flex the artificial muscles of Mobots at ever-increasing distances. And as this has come about the men who "sit in the driver's seat" have continued to have the strange feeling of being wherever the robot is.

Control center for deep-sea diving robot. Human operator at television console controls Mobot hundreds of feet below surface.   *Shell Oil Co.*

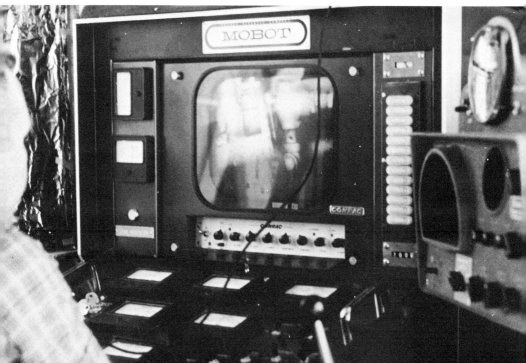

THE ROBOTS ARE HERE

The idea of the man-machine combination is not new. Old-time aviators, who flew by the seat of their pants, had the feeling that the airplane was simply an extension of their own arms and legs. The operator of the steam shovel or crane comes to know the same "feeling at a distance." The Mobot extends the range of such action, and it may eventually reach out thousands of miles. Engineers suggest that the first "men" on the moon may be robots, but men will have the feeling of actual discovery and of "being there."

Exploration of space by robots is a fact. Soon a robot called "Surveyor" will set down gently on the moon and investigate its surface. Robot "lunar rovers" have been the subject of much study and development in the past few years. We shall meet them again in our discussion of robot spacemen.

7
Robot Spacemen

The idea of mechanical helmsmen or pilots is not new, as we found out earlier from the robot ship in *Frithiof's Saga*. Although the robot in that early story was fictional, real robot pilots have been with us for some time. We have discussed autopilots that keep ships on course and fly airplanes swiftly and accurately.

Even for two-dimensional navigation the robot is a worthwhile member of the crew for several reasons. Perhaps the human trying to steer a big ship across the ocean becomes tired or forgets to watch the compass closely. The automatic pilot doesn't have these human failings and will stick to the course until power is shut off or something mechanical goes wrong. The robot navigator is also faster than a human. On a ship traveling relatively slowly across the water this may not seem a very important factor. But today some advanced robot navigators with electronic computer brains and radar eyes are showing that they can safely plot a course through fog and darkness, even though there are many other ships in the area. Such help is even more useful in an airplane streaking along at fifteen hundred or two thousand miles an hour.

The helmsman of a ship has to keep it headed in the right direction; he is responsible for movement along just one axis of the ship. An airplane can not only turn right or left, it can also nose up or down and roll from side to side. So while a good human pilot doesn't sleep and let the robot fly unattended, most pilots are content to relax and watch while the robot flies the plane.

Electronic navigational computers keep track of distance and direction, supplementing this "dead-reckoning" navigation with radio and radar ears, and eyes that take star sights and calculate a "fix" almost instantly. A good human navigator takes several minutes to do this.

Now we come to another kind of travel and to the question of whether the robot pilot and navigator has a place in it. When the first "Sputnik" reached into space a new age began, and soon we realized that space travel would need all the help it could get from robots. There are a number of reasons for this, but let's start with those we have already discussed in relation to ships and airplanes.

PROBLEMS IN SPACE

Just as airplanes travel much faster than ships, so satellites and space vehicles travel faster than planes. At six-hundred miles an hour a plane is going thirty times as fast as most ships; a satellite orbiting earth is moving thirty times as fast again and covering ten miles in just two *seconds* instead of the minute a plane would take!

Then too, navigation in space is much harder than "flat" navigation. While the human mind can grasp and perform the calculations needed for terrestrial flight if the speeds aren't too great, it falls down on the problem of *three* dimensions, especially since a space ship can't be slowed to a walk while the navigator thinks things out. So robots will undoubtedly help navigate space ships to their destinations and then perform most of the complex orbital maneuvers and actual landings.

Scientists have been concerned about the effects weightlessness will have on man. We are still not sure, although astronauts seem to have little difficulty during the relatively short flights they make. But the robot is unhampered by the lack of gravity. In fact, it is little affected by most of the problems that human space travelers must consider.

Electronic brain that can solve a trajectory problem for a lunar mission involving 36,000,000 calculations in an hour.

Minneapolis-Honeywell Regulator Co.

THE ROBOTS ARE HERE

Space travel also includes dangers from cosmic rays, the mysterious radiation that reaches earth from distant stars. Unshielded by the atmosphere, men in space are subjected to this cosmic bombardment. Yet another danger lies in the Van Allen belts—huge rings of intense radiation that circle the earth. These high-energy particles have played havoc with electronic equipment launched into space, and man himself has added to the danger by exploding nuclear devices high in the air. Instead of the fallout we are usually concerned with, these explosions left their debris of deadly radioactive dust hundreds of miles high, and silenced a number of satellites almost immediately.

Added to these dangers are those from powerful "solar flares" that erupt from the sun periodically and shoot dangerous radiation toward earth. These phenomena are harmful to equipment, and it is likely that they will harm men too. It may be necessary to shield our astronauts with sheets of lead; this will certainly be necessary when we put nuclear power in our space ships and satellites.

We have mentioned that some equipment has been damaged by radiation in space, but surely it will be easier to protect a robot than a human astronaut. Even if the robot is seriously damaged or completely knocked out, it is far better that it be sacrificed than one of us. And quite possibly robots will eventually be designed that will be impervious to almost anything encountered in space.

Another, more familiar kind of radiation is heat. Space is usually thought of as freezing cold, but heat is also dangerous there. For example, as our "Mariner" space probe approached Venus, increasing temperature almost put vital equipment out of commission. It surely would have harmed men had they been aboard. Here is another advantage of the space robot.

Cold can, of course, make man extremely uncomfortable and even kill him. This could happen in space during the shadowed portion of flight. The robot, on the other hand, can withstand the cold. Cryogenic (very low-temperature) devices are among the advanced electronic equipment being developed.

Except for deadly radiation and extremes of heat and cold, there is little else in space, and therein lies another great problem. Humans are creatures of long habit, and the most ingrained of these habits are breathing, eating, and drinking. Astronauts must take along their own atmosphere; but the robot can be designed to work in the "hard vacuum" of space. Some of its parts may have to be pressurized, and lubrication seems to be a tougher job in space. But in general the robot doesn't suffer from lack of oxygen or air-conditioning. It doesn't need food or water either, but can pluck electrical power right out of thin space by using solar batteries.

Time is also a human factor in space travel. Even a trip to nearby planets will take months or years, and as long again to return. When we think about voyaging out of the solar system, we suddenly realize that such a journey would consume a good chunk of a man's life span. We may face the choice of sending along a child who will be a man by the time he reaches his destination, or a robot to whom twenty years or more isn't important!

THE ROBOTS ARE HERE

ROBOTS IN ORBIT

Considering all these factors it is easy to see why much of the work done in space so far has been by robots. Perhaps the simplest space robot is "Vanguard I," a tiny satellite the size of a grapefruit. All it does is beep signals to radio receivers on earth, but these signals are very useful to geographers and geophysicists. Vanguard has helped scientists to determine the shape of the earth, and also to map some areas accurately for the first time. "Tiros" is a robot meteorologist that automatically takes pictures of global weather and televises them back to earth. "Midas" is a robot sentry that watches for launchings of enemy guided missiles.

Robots in earth satellites have helped pave the way for space travel by mice, monkeys, and finally men. But so far only robots have journeyed to the moon. Russia's "Lunik" was a remarkable robot space vehicle that photographed the dark side of the moon to prove it wasn't really dark at all, but pretty much like the side the moon turns to us. Our own "Lunar Orbiter" will take pictures of the moon automatically and relay them back to earth. "Ranger" is a robot television cameraman that failed in early attempts to take close-up pictures of the moon's surface. Other Rangers were more successful.

Man is hot on the heels of the robot spacemen. Manned orbital flights are no novelty and the next step into space will be a journey to the moon. "Apollo" may soon set men down on the moon and bring them safely home. But before that the robots will have been there checking up for us. The first "man on the moon" will in all probability be the mechanical one called Surveyor.

MECHANICAL MAN ON THE MOON

Built by Hughes Aircraft Company for NASA, Surveyor is designed to make a landing on the moon and then do just what its name suggests—survey the terrain. Surveyor will do no moving about but will investigate its surroundings and report its findings back to earth. Its job of surveying the scene completed, it will remain there to greet the first humans to reach the moon.

The moon seems to be a big globe of rock whose surface could be dust, inches or even feet thick. Some people are worried because the first space ship touching lightly down on the moon's surface might not stop there but sink slowly down, down, and out of sight. So one of the first jobs of moon robots, or lunar rovers, as they have come to be called, will be to find out just what the surface is like and how best to rove about.

Space scientists have put in a great deal of time and thought on the problem, trying to make educated scientific guesses and to build the type of vehicle best suited to locomotion across the craters or dust of the moon. If dust covers

"Surveyor," a robot that will land on the moon and dig samples of its crust and analyze them.   *Hughes Aircraft Co.*

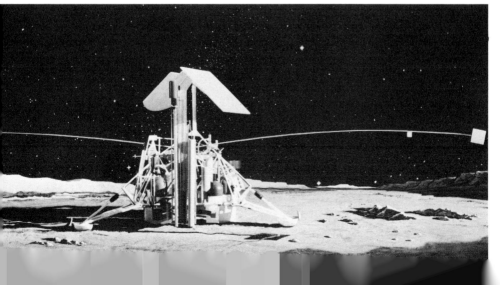

the moon, the rover may have to roll about on huge light wheels. But if the surface proves to be hard, the rover may be a robot with more conventional tires or wheels, or even a "walking machine" something like the pedipulators that General Electric is developing for the Army.

The lunar rover will in all probability be controlled from earth by men looking through the television eyes of the robot 240,000 miles away. The robot must move quite slowly, since it will take about three seconds for the earth operator to respond to what the robot sees on the moon. Clever stereo and color television methods have been proposed to provide the sense of perspective necessary for this very-long-range working of the controls. But somehow the job will be done, and the way will be paved for the humans who will follow the lunar rovers across the moon's surface. Then finally there will be some wild and exuberant leaps across the lunar terrain as human explorers know the thrill of lessened gravity!

Robot space vehicles have already probed far beyond the moon. Mariner navigated within about twenty thousand miles of Venus after an amazing flight of millions of miles, and it will be followed by other Mariner and "Voyager" robot spacecraft launched at Mars and Venus. Men will soon follow some of these journeys, but just as the robot may be the only means of exploiting inner space far beneath the ocean's surface, it may well be the only way to accomplish a number of the dangerous space journeys scientists have planned. We send probes like Pioneer close to the sun, for example, where the heat would be intolerable to man. For all these reasons, then, the robot is well assured of a place in space.

8
Electronic Brains

Early robots, the real mechanical men and not those in fiction, were empty-headed, frankly "brainless." Writers of fiction had realized the limitations of their mechanical men and dreamed up ways of endowing them with brains. Some authors felt that a mechanical brain was not possible and solved the problem neatly by borrowing a living brain from a luckless human victim. This required a miraculous surgical feat that somehow linked millions of connections from the human brain to the artificial "nerves" and "muscles" of the robot—but in fiction *anything* is possible.

For a long time real robots made no such dramatic mental strides. At best they could "remember" things. A clock alarm is a simple memory device, and clock mechanisms and arrays of switches and relays make up the memories of household robots like the washing machine and dishwasher.

ROBOT THINKER

Back in the 1940's a new device paved the way for another generation of robots. This new development was the electronic computer we have already mentioned briefly. Called an electronic brain, the early computer was really not especially bright but it was *very* fast. While we would be putting pencil to paper to begin adding a column of figures, it would be proudly printing out an answer.

There are two basic kinds of computers: the "analog," or

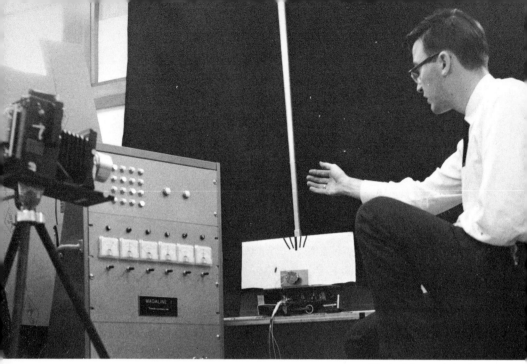

Stanford Research Institute

Balancing a broom is one of many accomplishments of MADALINE, a robot with an electronic brain.

measuring stick computer, and the "digital," or counting computer. A slide rule is a simple analog because it represents quantities with a physical length. An adding machine is a digital computer because it adds one and one and one, or deals in digits. The living brain is a kind of digital computer. It is a collection of neurons, tiny switches that are either on or off like a computer's switches. And it was the electronic digital computer that promised to make the robot a true thinking mechanical man.

Because an electronic brain is composed of switches that have just two positions—on or off—it uses a different kind of arithmetic from that with which we are familiar. Our decimal system uses ten numbers; the computer system uses only two. This is called "binary" arithmetic and the two values are generally represented by 1 and 0. These numbers correspond to the on and off positions of the switches.

The earliest electrical robot computing machines used simple switches. Later models employed electromechanical switches or relays. Then came electronics and vacuum tubes. Finally, transistors and other advanced devices were built into circuits, including "flip-flops" and "gates." One surge of electrical current sets the flip-flop in one position, the next flips it to the other position, in a pattern something like a see-saw. Such electronic switches perform the arithmetic in robot computing machines. And they also do *more* than arithmetic.

Early electronic computers were called giant brains, and it is easy to understand why. ENIAC, the first one, weighed thirty tons and covered a floor space twenty-five by forty-five feet. BINAC, which came along a little later, required a hundred and eighty kilowatts of electricity to operate, and an air conditioner with a capacity of fifty-two tons to keep it cool. Scoffers pointed to such huge size as proof that the robot's brain was hopelessly impractical—engineers have succeeded by thinking small. However, the electronic brain is being shrunk in size at the same time that it is growing in complexity and number of elements.

About the middle of the nineteenth century, a mathematician named George Boole invented a new kind of algebra. He called it a logical algebra, and instead of plus and minus he substituted the terms "true" and "false." Instead of mathematical tables, logical algebra uses "truth tables" and with it we can solve problems in logic. The designers of electronic brains adopted logical algebra for computer circuits, and the result was that the earlier "on" and "off" switches became parts of new circuits called "and," "or," and "nor" gates.

Our brains solve logical problems in just the way logical algebra does. Just as we add dollars and cents, we can add true and false facts and reach correct conclusions. With logic circuits, robot brains can do the same thing, and they do it far more quickly than we can!

Of course no electronic computer approaches the marvelous complexity of our brain, and in all probability none ever will. Author Capek "grew" his robots for *R.U.R.* in great vats of material similar to human body material. Only in fiction is such a thing possible—the computer's brain must depend on relatively crude electronic equipment.

Into an area of about one-tenth of a cubic foot, nature has packed *ten billion* neurons, or nerve cells, to make the human brain. As an illustration, let's say that some robot builders learn how to make a good artificial neuron of transistors, or more advanced devices. What might such a marvelous "brain cell" cost? A hundred dollars would be a good guess. But let's assume that, by an engineering miracle similar to the scientific miracle of duplicating the neuron, someone should produce individual brain cells for only a *dime* each. Even at such a ridiculously low price, the neurons for *one* artificial brain would cost *a billion dollars*! And there would still be the impossible job of assembling them properly, with some requiring not just one interconnection but dozens. The bill for one robot's "manlike" artificial brain

Artificial nerve net known as MIND: a Magnetic Integrator Neuron Duplicator.

would probably equal the national debt! So we cannot afford such a luxury, particularly because one robot would not be too useful.

Obviously we must settle for something less than the equivalent of a human brain. How about an artificial brain with only one billion neurons? Or a million? Even so puny an artificial brain, one ten-millionth as powerful as man's, strains today's technology, and robot's brains must be much simpler.

THE ROBOTS ARE HERE

Fortunately for the makers of robots, even the two-cell and six-cell brains of Dr. Walter's ELMER and CORA perform far better than might be expected; and with more elements their performance goes up encouragingly. Some robot airline reservation systems use as many as half a million transistors and other parts.

Some robots can operate with what is called "soldered" learning—that is, built-in knowledge. Their interconnections are made in such a way that when certain switches close, a desired action takes place. Still more advanced robots can cope with changing conditions and problems as they arise. Examples are robot-controlled power plants that do the logical "thinking" necessary for the safe and efficient operation of their equipment. Such systems work like this: Are customers calling for power? If so, check boilers for correct water level. If water is low, open inlet valve. Close when level is correct. Is fuel available for burners? If not, sound alarm bell. If fuel is available, open valve. Actuate igniter. Did fuel ignite? If yes, monitor steam pressure. If no, actuate igniter again. If fuel still does not ignite, shut off valve and sound alarm. When steam pressure reaches proper level, turn on generating equipment. Close switches to circuits needing power. Record amount of power to various customers and prepare bills.

The fire-control center at a missile base is another example of a logical robot. The robot's electronic circuits note whether or not a target is within range, whether the target is hostile, whether the target is moving slowly enough for the use of Missile A, or will require faster Missile B. If Missile A, is one of these ready on the launcher? Are all personnel clear of the area? Has the officer in charge pressed the OK button? Has the White House given permission to fire? and so on. Only a robot can evaluate all these yes-no questions fast enough for our high-speed weapons systems.

MACHINES THAT LEARN

Another kind of problem that can't be solved in logical fashion is called an *alogical* problem. As a simple example, our own learning of what certain things mean is not at all logical. Seeing and understanding the alphabet is a typical problem of learning by trial and error. Nothing in a baby's mind tells it instinctively that a single vertical line is the letter I; he must be taught this. Adults also must be taught certain things, or must learn them through trial and error. For a long time many computer and robot experts claimed that

"Cybertron," a learning machine that recognizes spoken sounds.

Raytheon Co.

no machine could ever handle this sort of problem, but in the last few years other scientists and engineers have proved them wrong.

Much learning is a matter of perceiving—seeing and recognizing a thing for what it is or represents. A psychologist named Frank Rosenblatt, working at Cornell University, thought he could make a machine that would perceive. He did just that, and named his new robot "Perceptron." One of the first things Perceptron "learned" was to recognize the letter C (it was studying at Cornell!). While this doesn't sound like any award-winning accomplishment, the *way* Perceptron did it was actually a tremendous step toward science-fiction's dream of thinking robots. Instead of wired learning, Perceptron's brain used electronic nerve cells connected in a random manner. As it learned, it "organized" this network of cells itself—something no mechanical brain had done before. Perceptron accomplished this organizing by selecting circuits on a trial-and-error basis, being rewarded or punished, and correcting its decisions if necessary.

Our brains, while millions of times more complex and wonderful than the most advanced Perceptron, are thought to be somewhat random networks when we are born. Thus we are able to learn those things necessary to us in the place and at the time we live. Humans learn things today very different from those they learned a hundred years ago, and those of us in America learn things different from those people learn in foreign lands. We are called "self-organizing systems" by scientists, and their goal is to make robots self-organizing too.

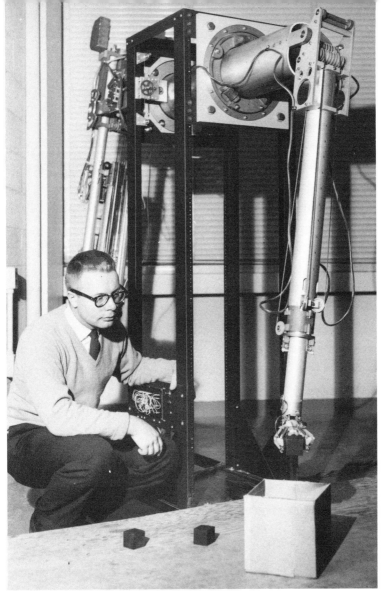

Robot hand plays with blocks and stores them in box.

Soon after Perceptron, another learning robot was built by the Raytheon Company. Called "Cybertron," it was designed specifically to solve the alogical type of problem. This it does with the help of a "goof button" in its side. When Cybertron makes a mistake, a human teacher pushes the goof button and the robot corrects its mistake. Among other things, it has learned to identify the sounds of submarines on a sonar recording and to identify and print out all the sounds of the human voice. Its builders stress the fact that Cybertron is a "learning" robot that can solve problems a computer with built-in knowledge could not.

Interesting things happen when these new and inquisitive robot brains are coupled to the mechanical portions of a machine. To a mechanical hand and arm of the type used for industrial robots Dr. Heinrich Ernst of Massachusetts Institute of Technology added a special electronic computer, to create what he called the first robot with an idea of what is going on in the outside world. Instead of following a set routine when turned on, the robot explores the area within its reach in a searching fashion. When it meets an obstacle, it maneuvers around it with no human help. Finding a wooden block, it determines its shape and size and then sets out to find another which it stacks on top of the first. If it encounters an open box too large for it to pick up, it reaches inside, like a child exploring the cookie jar, to see if it will hold the blocks already located. While this simple hand is a far cry from a manlike robot that can get about in the world, it is a modest start.

In trying to find a way to make a brain for robots it was natural that scientists study the human brain for clues. The benefit gained by doing the reverse is not so obvious. In laboratories all over the world scientists are studying the electronic brain to gain insight into the way our own gray matter works.

In England Dr. Walter built his robots, ELMER and CORA, as primitive models of living brains. Another Britisher, Dr. W. Ross Ashby, who has since come to the United States, built a more complex mechanism called the "homeostat" as part of an investigation of how the nervous system achieves adaptive behavior. Today, for every new piece of knowledge learned by an engineer studying living brains, a similar fact is learned by the psychologist or physiologist who is studying artificial brains. The study of man-machine similarities and differences profits not just the robot, but humans as well.

Before the electronic brain, the robot was capable only of a kind of plodding type of "thought." Now, as we have seen, it can handle even complicated problems that involve learning, computations, evaluation of situations, and the making of decisions. Early robots substituted for man's muscles, but the newer ones are helping him to think.

9

Robots at Play

Man seems to have a universal liking for games. His brain was designed as a problem-solver, although some experts feel that man's problems are essentially those of staying alive and are not necessarily guaranteed to develop the smartest intellect. At any rate, for hundreds of years men have whiled away pleasant hours playing chess, checkers, ticktacktoe, cards, and other games.

Robots play games too, and they usually win. Since we have concluded that robots are meant to do useful work, it is hard to understand the use of expensive computer robots to play chess and checkers. American experts visiting Russia were asked by surprised scientists why the United States should waste expensive machines on such frivolities when there were real problems to be solved. It was a good question, but the answer, as we shall see, was even better—and Russian computers are playing chess now, too.

YEARS OF PRACTICE

Game-playing robots are not new, either. Back in the last century, Charles Babbage proposed building a computing machine that would play a game of ticktacktoe, or noughts and crosses, as our British cousins call it. Babbage, who went on to build the forerunners of modern computers, designed a machine that would be capable of playing not just a rigidly fixed game, but one in which the strategy would be random and a human opponent would have a hard time figuring out what move the machine was likely to make next. As an added touch, Babbage planned to have a mechanical rooster and a lamb on the machine, the one to crow over a win, and the other to bleat when it lost!

More recently, Edmund Berkeley built his electrical "Relay Moe," which played the game to perfection, or any degree of perfection desired. It could win or draw all the time or let a human opponent win a specified percentage of the games. Colored lights flashed as the game was played—red

Fleximan deals a hand of cards.   United Fleximation Corp.

for the machine, and green for the man. At game's end, a red, green, or white light was turned on, depending on whether Relay Moe won, lost, or drew the match.

The appeal of ticktacktoe is hard to understand, because the game looks so simple. However, more than fifteen thousand combinations are possible in the first five moves alone! Berkeley designed an electromechanical computer, now called "Brainiac," which sells for a few dollars and includes the game of ticktacktoe in its repertoire. Unlike Relay Moe, Brainiac plays an unyielding game and cannot be beaten if it has the first move.

Chess is obviously a more complex game than ticktacktoe, and those of us who can play it are proportionately fewer in number. The total of possible moves in chess is fantastically huge; 10^{120} different variations are possible in a single game. This is the number 1 followed by 120 zeroes! Even if a game-playing robot could investigate a move each millionth of a second, it would still take 10^{108} *years* to check all the possible results of its first move.

Not even a master chess player could investigate all these moves, and the remarkable achievement of a robot that, fifty years ago, could play even an "end game" is evident. Since then the machine has been improved a great deal, thanks in large part to the electronic computer.

During the 1940's the British mathematician A. M. Turing played chess with a computer called MADAM. However, MADAM was rated a "stupid" opponent. Claude Shannon of Bell Telephone Laboratories devised a program in 1950 for playing chess on an electronic computer. Considering the limitations of even a high-speed machine in the face of the overwhelming choice of possible plays, Shannon planned for a look-ahead of only two moves.

Within the next few years, an IBM 704 computer had been programmed to play a passable game of chess. In looking ahead two full moves, it investigates 2,800 positions and requires eight minutes to make up its "mind." Although the 704 plays well against an amateur, it is rated a weak player against a good opponent, particularly since it does not improve, and after having been beaten by a certain strategy, will lose again in the same manner.

The robot's advantages in playing chess are many. It does not forget, does not blunder because of eagerness, anger, or other emotions, and never gets tired. The machine has dis-advantages, too, at the present stage of its development. It shows no imagination and does not look ahead many moves as do master players. In 1957, a computer expert predicted that within ten years a machine would be the chess champion of the world. This has not happened so far, and scoffers like chess expert Emil Lasker say that such a prediction is preposterous. Time will prove who is right. Meanwhile the robot *checker player* is making a good showing for itself.

There are undoubtedly more competent checker players than those who play a good game of chess. The reason is simply that checkers is not as difficult as chess. All pieces are the same, at least at the start of the game, and moves are uniform instead of different for each piece, as in chess. Today's robots are better able to play such a game.

Dr. Arthur Samuel of International Business Machines has

International Business Machines Corp.

Dr. Arthur Samuel plays checkers with electronic computer.

taught an electronic brain to play checkers. While Samuel beat the machine at first, it soon began to beat him. Later it won games from a champion player. Unlike the chess-playing machine, it "learned." Instead of using the same strategy over and over, it roughly "copied" a human player who improves with experience by trying different strategies and remembering those that win. When such flexibility can be given to a robot chess player, it will be a more formidable adversary, and the day of the robot world champ will be that much closer at hand.

In still another game that dates far back in history, a game called Nim, players take objects from several stacks and try to make their opponent take "the last straw"—perhaps the origin of that meaningful expression. A seemingly trivial game, actually it taxes a keen brain. However, the proper selection of straws is easily solved by "binary" arithmetic in which only two values instead of our customary ten are used. Since "binary" is the mathematical language of the electronic computer, such Nim-playing machines are masters of the game. "Nimatron," built by Westinghouse, played 100,000 games at the New York World's Fair in 1940 and won 90,000 of them. The British-built robot called "Nimrod" bested all comers at the Festival of Britain in 1951.

THE IMPORTANCE OF GAMES

Perhaps the simplest game in the world is matching pennies. Electronic computers that match pennies with humans analyze the strategy their opponents use, in order to beat them. While the use of expensive electronic brains for so childish a pastime seems to be wasteful, there is excellent scientific reason for their use. The game of matching coins goes to the core of the laws of probability, laws important not just in games of chance, but in engineering, business, and even war.

Our chess-playing robots that puzzled Russian scientists also bother many of our own people, and there is a disagreement today between traditional military planners and the computer-using "whiz kids" in Washington. The truth is that playing games involves the solution of some of the knottiest problems of decision-making. And the machine is better suited to solve many of these kinds of logical and mathematical problems.

Man, for all his brain's ten billion neurons, is slow at logical reasoning. Take, for example, a problem of the "Smith,

THE ROBOTS ARE HERE

Jones, and Robinson" type, in which we are told various things about three men and asked to pick their occupations. Such brain twisters are sometimes used as tests for job candidates, and most of us have a difficult time solving them. But an electronic computer answers them immediately, and man is no match for a robot equipped with such an infallible, split-second brain.

Even the simplest robots can play games. MENACE is not an electronic brain nor even an electrical one. The letters stand for Matchbox Educable Noughts And Crosses Engine, and MENACE was built from three-hundred matchboxes and a heaping handful of colored beads. British psychologist Donald Michie built this game-playing robot to see if he could teach a simple machine to play ticktacktoe. In action, MENACE plays against its human opponent by means of colored beads drawn randomly from its matchbox "brain cells." It is rewarded for winning and punished for losing by having beads added or taken away following com-

Playing "Hexapawn" with unbeatable matchbox robot.

D. S. Halacy, Jr.

pletion of a game. How well it learns is evident in a record of the games played.

Michie played against his creation for two days, during which two hundred twenty games were played. After twenty games MENACE was playing perfectly against standard strategy and the psychologist resorted to varying his strategy to put MENACE into unfamiliar territory. After a hundred and fifty games, however, the matchbox brain won eight out of ten which Michie played in what he thought was the best way to beat the machine. He did plead fatigue, however! MENACE, of course, suffered from no such human frailty.

MENACE had "learned" during the process of the two hundred and twenty games played. Operating on an initial trial-and-error basis, as Michie points out animals are thought to act, the machine learned and was reinforced by reward and punishment, again as is the case with animal learning. Certainly its "brain cells" had changed in the process. Other matchbox robots have been taught to play Nim, the game of Go, and even a simplified version of checkers.

After educating MENACE, Michie went on to program big Ferranti computers to play ticktacktoe with a further refinement. Instead of playing against mere human opponents, the robot brains printed their O's and X's against one another! Playing at lightning speed, they learned at a fantastic rate and had soon exhausted the possibilities of ticktacktoe! Some experts foresee chess-playing robots that will compete with one another and quickly become far better than humans can ever hope to be.

THE ROBOTS ARE HERE

If you should see a computer robot matching pennies or playing some other game, remember that its activity is not as frivolous as it may seem. By mastering the laws of chance and the principles of logical reasoning it is becoming a better aid for engineers and scientists, as well as for soldiers, lawyers, doctors, and many others who are already using its services gladly.

10

Robot on the Payroll

The robot is a wonderful device. It can do many things we can do—and some we cannot do. Some people feel that most of the world's woes could be solved by having more of these mechanical helpers to do our work for us. Others' feelings about mechanical men are just the opposite. We should therefore give careful consideration both to praise for robots and warnings against their use.

Some who argue against robots see the working man caught in the middle and pressed from both sides by the two powerful forces of science and industry. Science is producing the robot, and industry wants to use it. What effect has this had upon human beings, and what additional effects will it have over a long period of time? Ever since automation and the robot-run factory became a reality instead of a figment of science fiction, many thoughtful people—and some not so thoughtful—have been concerned with the problem. Tons of material have been published on both sides of this argument. While one group points to the achievements of robots, the other is concerned that the machine is displacing enough workers to cause widespread unemployment—technological unemployment, as it is called.

Stories continue to be written pointing out the terrible danger the robot poses to man. The novel *Player Piano* describes what happened when robots took over and left many

Punched card program goes into robot ice-cream maker controlled by computer.

people jobless, with time on their hands they could not fill in any satisfactory way. The book ends with a brutal revolt of human workers against the machines and their masters. Fear of the robot as an evil menace, expressed in stories like *Frankenstein* and *R.U.R.*, still troubles many people. One way of evaluating their menace is to look back into history again, and compare the hostile reception the early machines met with to their effect upon our society since then.

THE ROBOT'S RECORD

Even before Monsieur Jacquard invented his punched-card controls for looms, the weaving industry had encountered the controversial idea of machine versus man. We have learned about the War of 1812 between America and England, but may not know that there was another war that year, when English textile manufacturers introduced machinery which included the automatic gig-mill and shearing frame. Weavers saw in these a loss of jobs for themselves and rose up angrily against the new mechanical workers. This was the "Luddite" revolt.

We may recall also that the invention of printing presses caused riots when scribes feared they would be put out of work. In reprisal they demolished the machines and even stoned inventors so that they might continue to ply their trade with their traditional quill pens.

Eli Whitney's cotton gin was a target for destruction by workers who saw in it a threat to their security. More recently, the mechanical cottonpicker was subjected to a barrage of stones when it made its appearance in the fields and snatched the white bolls from the plants at a rate that made human pickers seem to move like snails.

We usually associate the term *saboteur* with destructive acts in wartime to harm an enemy. But the expression comes from Belgian workers who long ago tossed their wooden shoes into the gears of machines in factories, in the vain hope they could chase away the mechanical threat. But they succeeded in losing shoes as well as jobs.

Whaling was once a vast American industry as well as a base for romantic literature of the sea and the men who sailed it. Thomas Edison wrecked this industry most effectively with his invention of the electric light. Who wanted to read by sputtering whale oil lamp when the bright new miracle was available?

We can understand how workers must have felt when they saw machines taking their jobs. But over the years, are we worse off for having automatic machines? Would it be better if the rioters had won, and books were still written by scribes with quill pens, and cloth woven by hand? Do we have a vast army of unemployed cotton-pickers languishing in the South and the West because of the machines, or are these people now doing something else, perhaps something more interesting and rewarding?

A MAKER OF JOBS

What has actually happened is that instead of wiping out jobs, the robot has created *more* of them. When men are replaced in a factory, they will most likely find other jobs scattered through a dozen new factories that then spring up. Stories may depict idle workers sitting around eating their hearts out because the leisure afforded by machines is boring them to tears. But though some of us might look eagerly toward the happy situation of having time to do anything we want, this has not yet been the result of the robot takeover. To maintain our increasing standard of living and to spread

This machine-tool robot is milling a helicopter gearbox cover.

it through the world, may require that everybody work as long hours as ever, despite the high efficiency and increased output of automation.

The telephone is an example. As central switchboards and dial phones came along and some operators were let go, many people forecast the day when nobody would work for the telephone company—nobody, that is, but the machines. This, happily, has not come about, and the telephone industry, surely one of the biggest users of machines, hires more people all the time as its services expand.

The use of machines has made more material things available to more of us humans. Machines have made it possible to grow more crops to feed the exploding population the world is faced with these days. And far from creating a leisure class, they are causing a shortage of educated help. For example, there are not enough scientists, engineers, and technicians being turned out in our schools to fill the demands of research and industry.

All these things point up an important fact that has not been properly understood in the past. Almost a hundred years ago an official in the United States Patent Office suggested that his organization might as well be shut down since surely all important inventions had been made and the world could coast merrily along without inventors! His mistake is now obvious; the big problem the Patent Office has today is not one of justifying its existence, but keeping from drowning in the sea of new ideas. What has happened, of course, is that each invention has set the stage or created the need for two or a dozen more. Television comes to mind as an example. Far from being the end, it was the beginning of a whole new branch of developments. Black and white television was not enough; we now have color. Performers are helped with an invention known as the Teleprompter, and we also have innovations like airborne broadcasting and orbiting satellites that carry television around the world.

The airplane was looked upon as a single invention by many people—an end in itself. What has happened instead? In addition to original patents, there have been hundreds, perhaps thousands, of other patents growing out of the basic idea of the airplane. The jet engine is one outgrowth of the original invention; others are the helicopter and the air-cushion car. Airplane wings have slots and flaps to make them more efficient. Planes flying from carriers have deck-

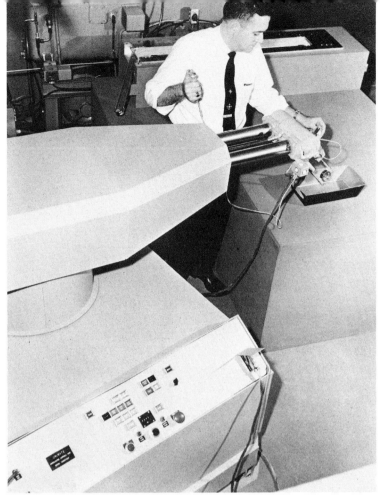

Supervisor teaching Unimate a new job that the robot learns perfectly the first time.

hooks to stop them more quickly and catapults to get them into the air faster. One idea generates other ideas.

The same thing happens with robots. The electronic brain was feared by many as being a device that would shortly solve all mathematical problems and thus eliminate the jobs this vast field provides. Nothing could be more ridiculous. The robot mathematician simply makes it possible for the scientist to tackle problems that up to now he has thought of only wistfully because his human brain could not perform all the operations necessary in its lifetime. Even the fastest machines can hope to do only a tiny fraction of the problems human brains can think up! The more we know, the more there is to learn. No one can foresee the day when we will know all about this world; and already we are probing *other* worlds.

The men who used to pick cotton by hand are now driving mechanical pickers. Cotton once wasted on the ground is reclaimed economically by robot pickers with rubber fingers. Mill owners are ever on the lookout for even more efficient mechanical weavers and spinners to turn out enough cloth to clothe the world. And automatic presses have not made jobless tramps of the printers who once set type by hand. Instead there are far more men working in the printing field than ever before as demand for the products of the automatic presses increases. Where once a machine took over for a hundred men, we now need machines to do the work of a thousand, because it seems there is ten times the work to be done to satisfy our increasing demands and the eventual needs of the poorer nations of the world.

NO TURNING BACK

We can look at the problem from another angle too. What would happen if the robots were suddenly taken from us? If man attempted to do their work himself rather than let them do it, certainly he could not maintain his present standard of living or anything close to it.

In all probability we will keep on along the road to more and more use of machines. It would be foolish, nevertheless, not to realize that the robot does bring with it some big problems that must be solved. If a human worker is forced to compete with a robot he is bound to suffer. If the printer of old had had to sell his books at the prices the mechanized press now makes possible, he could have worked twenty-four hours a day and still have starved to death. The factory worker of today who tries to compete on the labor market with a robot is whipped before he begins.

The answer seems to be not to compete, but to let the robot do those things it can do more cheaply than man. In the process, men are being displaced, some of them painfully. And we must use great care to hurt the smallest number of individuals as little as possible as we continue to change from muscle power to machine power, and from human brains to robot brains. With common sense and a humane approach, it can be done. When installation of new robot equipment will make the services of many human operators unnecessary, the displaced or replaced persons must be shifted to *newer* jobs.

Some factory owners and business men have found that normal turnover of employees can take care of positions lost to machines. In other words, during a year a certain number of people will retire or leave a company for various reasons. Women marry and become homemakers, others already married leave to raise families. Of course, it can be argued that people are still being put out of work—those just coming out of school and looking for jobs to get started

THE ROBOTS ARE HERE

in. But these newcomers can be fitted into the new and different jobs machines are helping to create.

There are always two sides to an argument. While one group deplores automation as inhuman, another may rightly ask what the alternative is. At this late date we cannot go back to a farming or hunting civilization: there are too many of us. We live in a world that is increasingly mechanized, of necessity. It is also painfully true that while automation may improve jobs, it does not of itself improve individual workers! Such a step must be taken by the worker himself, or, more wisely it is to be hoped, by society. There are indications that this is the course we shall take.

Our government is quite naturally concerned with the impact of the robot because although it helped pioneer the use of machines, it is also our biggest employer of human help. Government committees have been appointed to study the problem of integrating men and machines and to find solutions. This is a step in the right direction. So too are joint industry and labor investigations like that between United States Industries and the American Federation of Labor, described earlier in connection with dues-paying robots.

There are fewer human ditchdiggers today and more men running machines. There are fewer file clerks than there were before electronic robots began to process information. But there are more office workers in more responsible positions, overseeing the work of robot clerks. The industrial revolution saw the substitution of metal and fuel for human muscle; the intellectual revolution is substituting electronic brains for human brains.

Perhaps the robot is indeed a jobstealer. But the jobs it steals are not the challenging ones, and the problem caused by this loss of jobs is small today, compared to the havoc that would be created if suddenly all robots were eliminated. We must keep our mechanical hired hands because we need them to run our modern world in the fashion to which we have become accustomed.

11

The Robot's Future

Even though the robot was thought of and mentioned in our literature thousands of years ago, real mechanical men have a far shorter history, and only recently have they actually gone to work for us. The robot's progress has not been as obvious or as spectacular as that of the airplane, but potentially the robot may be more important, since it not only flies a plane, but minds the baby, translates Russian into English, and builds other robots!

Today the robot army is modest—though perhaps it is larger than we realize. Until a century or so ago men were able to get along mostly on muscle power, using their own hands and capable brains to take care of problems that came up. But today's world is far more complicated than that of 1850, and tomorrow's will make the present seem like horse and buggy days. The guesses of the most optimistic dreamers may be just as accurate as the best-informed predictions of our ablest automation scientists—it is often hard to tell them apart. Reporting on an interview with one of these scientists, a newsman wrote that if he hadn't known who the gentleman was he would have sneaked away and phoned a mental institution!

Just for fun let's make some guesses about the world of A.D. 2000. Our homes will be as much advanced over those we now live in as these are ahead of a log cabin. Instead of a building that requires constant attention from its owners, the home will be more like a living thing, capable of taking care of its own needs as well as of those of its occupants. Automatically and completely air-conditioned, it will maintain the correct temperature and humidity while at the same time being economical with fuel. Drapes and curtains will open and close as the sun rises and sets or as storms occur. In balmy weather windows will open by themselves. Doors will open at our approach, and close when we have passed. They will lock automatically at night.

The kitchen will make the one we work in now seem like a sweatshop by comparison. Meal-planning and shopping will be done by our robot housekeeper, as will the cooking, dishwashing, and general cleanup. Bedmaking, dusting, vacuuming, window-washing, and other workaday chores will be done automatically. We will control the television set by talking to it, or let it automatically turn on our favorite programs so we don't forget them. Yardwork will be done by a robot gardener, and "house power" will come from a roof that catches the sun's rays and converts them to electricity.

We will ride to work in a robot-controlled car that knows where we want to go and takes us there quickly and safely with its electronic eyes, brain, and steering mechanism. If we ride a train or plane or ship, there may be no human crew except for stewards and stewardesses to give it that "old-fashioned" touch we enjoy. It will be comforting to know that accidents have almost completely vanished, although it may hurt our human pride a little to realize that robots are much better drivers and pilots than we were.

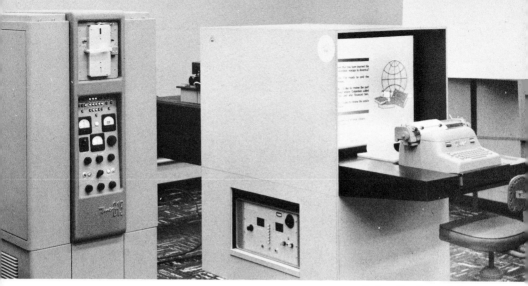

System Development Corp.
Teaching machine used in research into automatic instruction.

At school we will spend the morning in the electronic "classroom" where we learn from lectures and three-dimensional color films, with immediate answers to all our questions as we ask them. The "classroom" will be linked electronically with robot libraries and other centers around the world. Even as we are learning, our progress will be recorded and evaluated so that our future learning can be planned properly and any important ideas or discoveries we may make will be available for the benefit of others.

We will have lunch in the automat, one of the oldest robot examples we can remember. It will be somewhat different from those of the 1960's, of course. Seating ourselves at a table we scan the menu and are soon treated to the delicious smells of the dishes we ordered, delivered automatically to our table through a food slot in the wall. When we leave, the dishes are whisked away before we have taken but a few steps.

Most of our shopping will be done at home by television,

but if we stop in at a shoe store, for example, we will settle in a comfortable chair, select the style we want from a chart, place our foot on a stand in front of us, and in seconds try on the desired shoe automatically. We will insert our identification card in a billing machine on the way out and have the purchase automatically recorded. The same card will be good for anything we may want to buy—for making bank deposits or withdrawals on the rare occasions that is necessary, and in our dealing with various branches of the government. The manager of the store nods courteously as we leave. An assistant is making some changes on one of the sample displays, and a technician is checking the control board of the automatic record-keeping robot.

Suppose we stop to see a friend who works in a factory whose products are radios and television sets, mostly for export. Our friend manages the testing department, and he shows us his "workers," hundreds of robots that busily run final checks on each piece of equipment before packing it. Although the plant is not teeming with human workers as in the old films we have seen in the electronic classroom at school, there are hundreds of them in various parts of the big factory. Even in the automatic factory, men and women must be on hand to oversee the robots.

In Washington, D. C., we still have a human President, of course, and a Congress and many thousands of other human government employees. But they too are aided by robots. Income taxes are processed by machines, and we remember that this started in the 1960's. Planning in all departments is aided by the electronic brain. Problems pertaining to road-building, commerce, and dozens of other activities important to our population of 350,000,000 are worked out by robot computers in a fraction of the time it would take the best human mathematicians. Social Security, veteran's affairs, foreign-aid programs, and military services all rely on help from the machines. No one human brain or group of brains can hope to evaluate the many factors in complex world problems, and make split-second decisions when a crisis arises. So robot brains are working all the time, using up-to-the-minute information from many sources to produce a continuous "best plan" for the use of the President and his assistants as they see fit.

In the year 2000, robot translators will still be busy, but we may hope that this chore will be remembered only as interesting history. This is because the robots will have made possible international cooperation to a degree once thought impossible.

Knowledge will spread around the world rapidly and ideas be shared much more quickly. Robot satellites will provide global weather reports almost on a minute-to-minute basis, and will transmit radio, television, and telephone communications as never before. All this will speed the day when the world's people will speak one language and truly understand one another.

The robot's many uses range from running our homes to running the world; there are other possibilities. Man was born with a curiosity that apparently will never be satisfied as long as there is any nook or cranny unexplored. Robots permit him to reach into dangerous environments on the

DASH, with its load of two homing torpedoes, lifts from the deck of USS Hugh Purvis.

earth, beneath its crust, and under the sea. But in space the robot truly comes into its own. We have discussed how admirably suited it is for this task, since it needs no air to breathe or food to eat. Withstanding radiation that endangers man, the robot explores for him at a distance, not only the planets of the solar system but the vast reaches beyond it. Man cannot live long enough to make a trip to a distant star, but a robot-controlled spaceship launched by earlier generations will permit him to explore to his heart's content.

"Simulation" is a task the electronic brain has already

THE ROBOTS ARE HERE

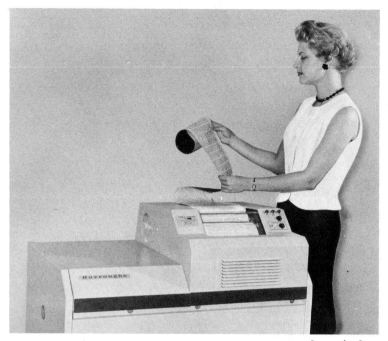

Burroughs Corp.

Robot printer transmits 3,000 words a minute for weather information and military messages.

proved it can do. Businesses, wars, and even storms have been simulated. Science-fiction writers have suggested the creation of a tiny world, a robot model of earth, able to evolve at a fantastic rate of speed. Perhaps long-range planning for earth will one day be done somewhat in this manner. Machines will create tiny robot worlds, accurately reproducing the factors to be studied. An engineer will push a button and in a few seconds a century of earth's future is unrolled and studied. If all works well, the plans under test may be put into practice. But if something goes haywire and the "earth" goes up in smoke, as it often does in fiction, the designer will be able to shake his head and go back to the drawing board for another try!

What will the robots of A.D. 2000 look like? Many will be strictly functional, with wheels where wheels are needed and a sense of smell only if that is important. Most of them will look nothing like the mechanical men that populate the films turned out in Hollywood and other movie capitals. But perhaps some of them will look far more human than even these fictional creatures. Walt Disney's World's Fair robots are a hint of what is possible. One early proposal for robots, both in fiction and in serious articles, was to use them as baby sitters. We may have a robot that is at once nurse, toy, pet, and guardian or teacher.

It may also be advantageous to have the robot look like a man—or woman—in a business that deals with the public. A manager of a complaint department would seem an ideal job for a robot that would never lose its temper, get upset, or be discouraged! Guides for various exhibits, waitresses, and guards are possible jobs for robots. So too are dancing instructors with feet that won't bruise, actors who give flawless performances each time, and clever sparring partners for boxers.

Quite seriously, the electronic brain has been suggested as a means of caring for the *human* brain. Some doctors think such robots will eventually be able to monitor their human patients skillfully and thus predict and ward off mental breakdowns. If such a medical robot were built in the form

of a handsome human doctor it would inspire more accept-
ance in the human patient than would a "black box" of electronic equipment.

The shape of things to come, as far as robots are concerned
then, depends on the uses for which they are intended. If it
is important that they look human, they will look as human
as we want them to. If some other shape is better, the robot
will take that shape. For example, a deep-space probe may
need a robot navigator, observer, and pilot to fit into a four-
inch cube and weigh no more than two pounds.

Our excursion into the year 2000 is fanciful, but these
things can and most likely will be done because of the rapid
progress being made on many technological fronts. We have
seen that the robot's brain has evolved dramatically in a few
years. It can learn new things and predict the future from
past happenings. There have always been realistic scientists
and engineers who have said that even if we could build a
brain equal to our human one, it would be so big that it just
wouldn't be practical. In 1851 an English doctor named
Smee described such a giant brain but sadly admitted it
would most likely cover an area about the size of London.
The robot builders had made so much progress by 1950 that
the argument was that such a brain would be the size of
the Pentagon and require a Niagara to power and cool it.
But another development has come along to shrink further
the monster brain of the robot.

Miniaturization has been popularized in many fields. The
Volkswagen is one example; the tiny transistor is a much
better one. Miniaturization seems to be the special province

of electronics. Aircraft and space vehicles are heavy users of electronic equipment, and the only way to keep putting more equipment aboard is to make it smaller and lighter. As a result, strange slogans prevail in many laboratories. "It has to be unseen to be appreciated," is typical, as are "Shrink Big" and "Think Small." Many an engineer is fearful of sneezing away the day's output of tiny components.

The transistor was a dramatic reduction in size from the older vacuum tube, but now something called integrated circuitry has come along. An entire radio amplifier fits into the space a single transistor once required. Instead of a case the size of the Pentagon, a typewriter case may soon hold enough artificial neurons to be equivalent to a human brain, and designers are thinking smaller and smaller by the day. As a result even the tiniest robots will mount quite intelligent brains.

Integrated circuitry requires techniques different from the soldering of long leads, or the tightening of nuts and bolts, to assemble the electronic parts for a midget radio receiver or an electronic computer. These techniques include depositing vapor films and the growing of crystals. But there is a more intriguing kind of "growing" that suggests itself and brings back the memory of the vat-grown robots in *R.U.R.*

A great deal of biological research in recent years has led to the discovery and attempted synthesis of the giant DNA molecules that seem to govern life. Much has been learned about DNA, the "blueprint" for cell growth, and men have even made crude copies of this substance. It was suggested, facetiously at first, that the DNA blueprint idea might be used to *grow* products in a factory. Fantastic as this seems, there is reason to believe it could be done. Living tissue already is being grown under laboratory control to produce food and other substances. Why not use the technique to "grow" things like golf balls, pencils, and radios?

More probable, however, is mechanical imitation of the growth of living things, in which a machine is "programmed" to reproduce itself. This has been done in the laboratory on a very simple scale and suggested as a production method. If it comes to pass, not only our food, but also our automobiles, television sets, and even our robots may become crops instead of products.

There are robots in our present and in our future. Many people think they represent grave danger to our human way of life; many others feel that the machine represents our only hope if the present growth of population and technology is to be maintained. A few people believe we should smash *all* machines, starting now, and others foresee not the destruction of the machines by man, but the evolution of man into machine.

Between these extreme views is the more realistic compromise of saying neither that man is superior to robot nor that robot is superior to man, but that the ideal is a man-machine combination far better than either of its parts. Some have called this "intellectronics," a coupling of intellect and electronics, and they predict that when man is free from his routine and time-consuming petty problems he can devote himself to those really worthy of his mind: problems of how best to get along with one another and assure that our powers are used to the best advantage of all.

We should not be like the shortsighted scoffer at space exploration who would rather that we just stayed home and watched television "the way God intended us to do!" The robot is a fact of our lives as are atom bombs, television, and space exploration. To deny that the machine poses problems is foolish, but to believe seriously that these problems force us to stop developing the machine is even more foolish. We may hope that robots will not be either slaves or deadly enemies, but helpful partners.

INDEX

INDEX

The Author

The Robots Are Here! is the result of D. S. Halacy's experience
with automation and computers, and his interest in the growing
importance of these "mechanical men" throughout history. After
graduation from Phoenix College and Arizona State University,
Mr. Halacy worked in the aircraft industry for several years and
served in both the Second World War and the Korean War as a
navigator in the Air Force.

Since the Korean War Mr. Halacy has specialized in writing
on engineering and in technical editing in the aircraft and electronics fields. He has been writing on a free lance basis since
1962. His published work includes light verse and prose humor,
short stories, articles, and novels, as well as some nonfiction
books. For ten years he has taught writing at Phoenix College.

D. S. Halacy was born in Charleston, South Carolina, and grew
up there, in New England, and in California. He now lives in
Glendale, Arizona, with his wife and two daughters.